World Clinics in Ophthalmology

Innovations in Primary Open Angle Glaucoma

Volume 2

Editor:
Samuel Boyd, MD

Guest Editors:
Maurice Luntz, MD, FACS
Deepak Mishra, MD
Juan Roberto Sampaolesi, MD

JAYPEE - HIGHLIGHTS
MEDICAL PUBLISHERS, INC.

JAYPEE - HIGHLIGHTS
MEDICAL PUBLISHERS, INC.
An Editorial Branch of Jaypee Brothers Medical Publishers (P) Ltd.

PRODUCTION
Production Director: Kayra Mejia
Chief, Digital Composition: Laura Duran, Erick Navarro
Art Director: Eduardo Chandeck
International Communications: Joyce Ortega

MARKETING
Director Sales & Marketing Latin America: Srinivas Chaubey
Customer Service: Miroslava Bonilla
Sales Manager: Tomas Martinez

World Clinics in Ophthalmology -
Innovations in Primary Open Angle Glaucoma
Editor: Samuel Boyd, MD
Guest Editors: Maurice Luntz, MD, FACS; Deepak Mishra, MD; Juan Roberto Sampaolesi, MD

ISSN 2224-1353

Published for: Jaypee - Highlights Medical Publishers, Inc.
City of Knowledge
International Technopark, Bldg. 237
Gaillard Highway, Clayton
Panama Rep. of Panama

Phone: (507) 301-0496 / 97 - Fax: (507) 301-0499
E-mail: cservice@jphmedical.com
Worldwide Web: www.jphmedical.com
Print and Bound in India

Acknowledgment

Nowadays, glaucoma still remains as one of the most important subspecialties in ophthalmology. Several surgical techniques offer the surgeons the opportunity to stabilize the intraocular pressure, the condition of the optic nerve as well as the visual field in the affected patient. Thus the importance of proper teaching of these procedures for specialists as well as practicing ophthalmologists and ophthalmologists in training.

The main aim of this book is to unveil the mysteries of glaucoma by presenting a panoramic view of the medical advances, the surgical procedures, medications and new technology for its different diagnosis. By far the best text in existence today offered by a group of first class authorities in the field.

We wish to express our deep appreciation to all the contributing authors of this first volume of the World Clinics in Ophthalmology, to our staff at Jaypee Highlights and of course to our dearest readers worldwide.

The Editors

Foreword

It is my sincere honor and privilege to introduce readers to a comprehensive and outstanding overview of state-of-the-art concepts in the diagnosis and management of primary open angle glaucoma. *World Clinics in Ophthalmology – Innovations in Primary Open Angle Glaucoma* incorporates recent advances, current practice patterns, and clinical highlights in the rapidly evolving field of glaucoma diagnosis and management. The book provides highly practical advice and timely instruction to assist the practitioner in treating a complex and challenging blinding disease. Furthermore, the information can be readily incorporated into the clinician's everyday practice.

The contributing authors to *World Clinics in Ophthalmology – Innovations in Primary Open Angle Glaucoma* are internationally renowned experts in their respective fields. They should be greatly commended for sharing their expertise with clinical pearls and techniques, as well as clear and concise summaries of the outlined topics. Innovative diagnostic and therapeutic technologies are presented in a succinct manner. In addition, the chapters are supplemented with outstanding color illustrations, figures, and photographs.

James C. Tsai, M.D., M.B.A.
Robert R. Young Professor and Chairman
Department of Ophthalmology and Visual Science
Yale University School of Medicine
Chief of Ophthalmology, Yale-New Haven Hospital

Editor

Samuel Boyd, MD
Director, Laser Section, and Associate Director,
Clinica Boyd - Ophthalmology Center
Panama, Rep. of Panama

Guest Editors

Maurice Luntz, MD, FACS
Clinical Professor of Ophthalmology, Mount Sinai School of Medicine, New York
Adjunct Clinical Professor of Ophthalmology, New York University
Medical School, New York – Former Director, Glaucoma Services,
Manhattan Eye, Ear and Throat Hospital
New York, NY, U.S.A.

Deepak Mishra, MD
Regional Institute of Ophthalmology (RIO) at the
Indira Gandhi Institute of Medical Sciences (I.G.I.M.S)
Patna, Bihar, India

Juan Roberto Sampaolesi, MD
Assistant Professor, Department of Ophthalmology, Faculty of Medicine,
University of Business and Social Sciences (UCES)
Buenos Aires, Argentina

Contributors

Eduardo Arenas A., MD, FACS
Fundacion Santa Fe y Sociedad de Cirugia Ocular
Bogota, Colombia

Augusto Azuara-Blanco, MD, PhD
The Eye Clinic, Aberdeen Royal Infirmary, University of Aberdeen.
Aberdeen, Scotland, U.K.

Benjamin F. Boyd, MD, FACS
Doctor honoris Causa Past President, Academia Ophthalmologica Internationalis
Past President, Pan-American Association of Ophthalmology
Honorary Life Member, International Council of Ophthalmology
Panama, Rep. of Panama

Anaika Concepcion, MD
Director, Glaucoma Department Clinica Boyd - Ophthalmology Center
Panama, Rep. of Panama

Mark A. Latina, MD
New England Eye Center, Tufts, New England Medical Center
Boston, MA, U.S.A.

Maurice Luntz, MD, FACS
Clinical Professor of Ophthalmology,
Mount Sinai School of Medicine, New York
Adjunct Clinical Professor of Ophthalmology, New York University
Medical School, New York – Former Director, Glaucoma Services,
Manhattan Eye, Ear and Throat Hospital
New York, NY, U.S.A.

Deepak Mishra, MD
Regional Institute of Ophthalmology (RIO) at the
Indira Gandhi Institute of Medical Sciences (I.G.I.M.S)
Patna, Bihar, India

Marlene R. Moster, MD
Glaucoma Service, Wills Eye Hospital
Philadelphia, PA, U.S.A.

Juan Roberto Sampaolesi, MD
Centro Oftalmologico Sampaolesi
Buenos Aires, Argentina

Roberto Sampaolesi, MD
Centro Oftalmologico Sampaolesi
Buenos Aires, Argentina

B.P. Sinha, MS
Regional Institute of Ophthalmology (RIO) at the
Indira Gandhi Institute of Medical Sciences (I.G.I.M.S)
Patna, Bihar, India

Joseph Anthony Tumbocon, MD
Massachusetts Eye and Ear Infirmary, Harvard Medical School
Boston, MA, U.S.A.

World Clinics in Ophthalmology
Innovations in Primary Open Angle Glaucoma
Volume 2

Contents

1 Selective Laser Trabeculoplasty

Mark A. Latina, MD
Joseph Anthony Tumbocon, MD

Concept

Argon laser trabeculoplasty was first described by Wise & Witter[1] in 1979 and has been viewed as an alternative to surgery in patients whose open angle glaucoma (OAG) could not be adequately controlled by medications. This treatment modality has been gaining popularity as an effective treatment option in patients with OAG as shown in the Glaucoma Laser Trial and Glaucoma Laser Trial Follow-up Study.[2] The investigators demonstrated that eyes treated initially with argon laser trabeculoplasty had lower intraocular pressures and better visual field and optic disk status than their fellow eyes treated initially with topical medications.

However, ALT has also been observed to produce some deleterious effects to the microstructure of the trabecular meshwork. Histopathologic studies have shown that argon laser trabeculoplasty results in coagulative destruction of the uveoscleral meshwork in the areas of the laser spots and causes heat-damage to the surrounding structural collagen fibers. Furthermore, a membrane formed by migrating endothelial cells was noted on the meshwork between the applied argon laser spots.[3,4,5,6] This membrane covering meshwork after argon laser trabeculoplasty (ALT) has been postulated to be the cause of late outflow reduction, pressure increase and treatment failure. Additionally, damage to the trabecular meshwork structure caused by ALT theoretically limits future medical and/or repeat laser treatment.

Selective Laser Trabeculoplasty (SLT) represents an improvement over conventional ALT by eliminating thermal damage of trabecular meshwork (TM) architecture. Using a low energy, Q-switched, frequency doubled Nd: YAG Laser emitting at 532 nm with a pulse duration of 3 nanoseconds, Latina, Park and Sibayan[7,8] demonstrated isolated destruction of the pigmented TM cells without producing any thermal nor collateral damage to the surrounding non-pigmented cells and trabecular collagen beams **(Figure 1)**. Furthermore, endothelial membrane formation on the TM, which is usually found in ALT treated eyes, was not observed after SLT exposure in vivo. These histologic findings were confirmed by Kramer and Noecker[9], where they compared the acute morphologic changes in the TM of human eye bank eyes after ALT and SLT by scanning and transmission electron microscopy. After laser irradiation, ALT produced crater formation, coagulative damage, fibrin deposition, disruption of trabecular beams and endothelial cells. SLT did not exhibit the aforementioned findings and the general structure of the TM was preserved. In contrast, the effect of SLT occurred in the intracellular level, wherein disruption of the melanin granules was observed. The lack of thermal and structural damage to the TM makes SLT potentially repeatable.

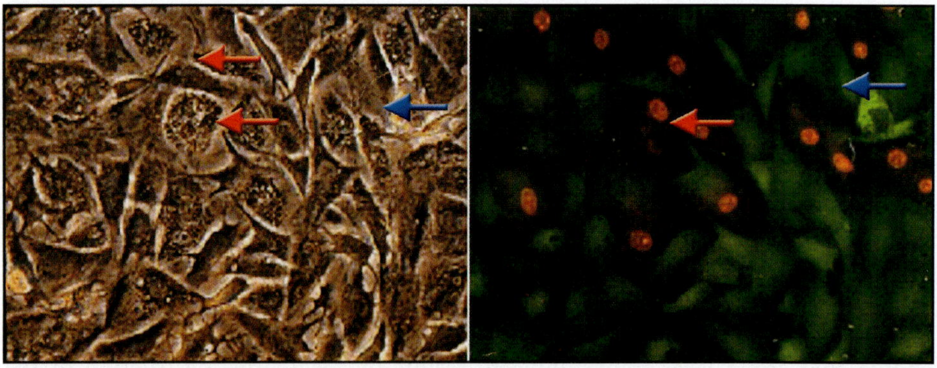

Figure 1: Figure on the Left: Phase contrast micrograph of pigmented and non-pigmented trabecular meshwork (TM) cells. Figure on the Right: Photomicrograph using fluorescent viability/ cytotoxicity assay after irradiation with SLT. Only the pigmented TM cells exhibited nuclear staining (orange fluorescence) and absence of cytoplasmic staining (green fluorescence) which indicate cell death (red arrow). The non-pigmented TM cells were not affected with SLT as shown by the presence of cytoplasmic staining and absence of nuclear staining in these cells (blue arrow) .

The in vitro and in vivo findings after SLT are observed because the pulse duration of SLT is much shorter (3 nanoseconds) than the thermal relaxation time of the target chromophore (melanin) in the pigmented TM cells.[7] Thermal relaxation time defines the absolute time required by a chromophore to convert electromagnetic energy in to thermal energy. Melanin has a thermal relaxation time of approximately 1 microsecond, while the pulse duration of the SLT is 3 nanoseconds. This means that the pulse duration of SLT is too short for the melanin to convert the electromagnetic energy to thermal energy and, thus, no heat is liberated. Therefore, this spares the surrounding non-pigmented tissues from any damage.

The IOP reductions observed after SLT provide an additional insight into the potential mechanism of IOP lowering after TM laser treatment. Selective trabeculoplasty is not associated with coagulation damage, yet it significantly lowers the IOP. This indicates that coagulation of the TM structure is not an important component to the mechanism of IOP lowering after SLT. The demonstrable clinical efficacy suggests that laser trabeculoplasty works on the cellular level, either through migration & phagocytosis of TM debris by the macrophages[10] or by stimulation of formation of healthy trabecular tissue which may enhance the outflow properties of the TM.[11,12] Alvarado[13] has observed a 5 to 8 fold increase in the number of monocytes and macrophages present in the trabecular meshwork of monkey eyes treated with SLT as compared with untreated controls. He theorized that injury to the pigmented TM cells after SLT results in the release of factors and chemo-attractants which recruit monocytes which are activated and transformed into macrophages upon interacting with the injured tissues. These macrophages then engulf and clear the pigment granules from the TM tissues exits the eye to return to the circulation via the Schlemm's canal.[14] All these events have been postulated to play a role in the IOP lowering effect of SLT.

Clinical Studies

In 1998, a pilot clinical study was conducted to evaluate the intraocular pressure lowering effect of Selective Laser Trabeculoplasty in 53 open angle glaucoma patients whose intraocular pressures could not be controlled with maximum medical therapy (Max Rx group) or had a previous failed argon laser trabeculoplasty (PFLT group).[15] Seventy per cent of the patients responded with an IOP reduction of at least 3 mmHg. At 26 weeks of follow up, the mean IOP reduction was 23.5% ($p<0.001$) for the Max Rx group, 24.2% ($p<0.001$) for the PFLT group, and 23.8% ($p<0.001$) for both groups combined (Figure 3). The promising results of this study led the investigators to embark on a prospective, multi-center clinical trial which involved 101 eyes of 101 patients in four clinical sites (Advanced Glaucoma Specialists, Reading MA; New York Eye and Ear Infirmary, New York,

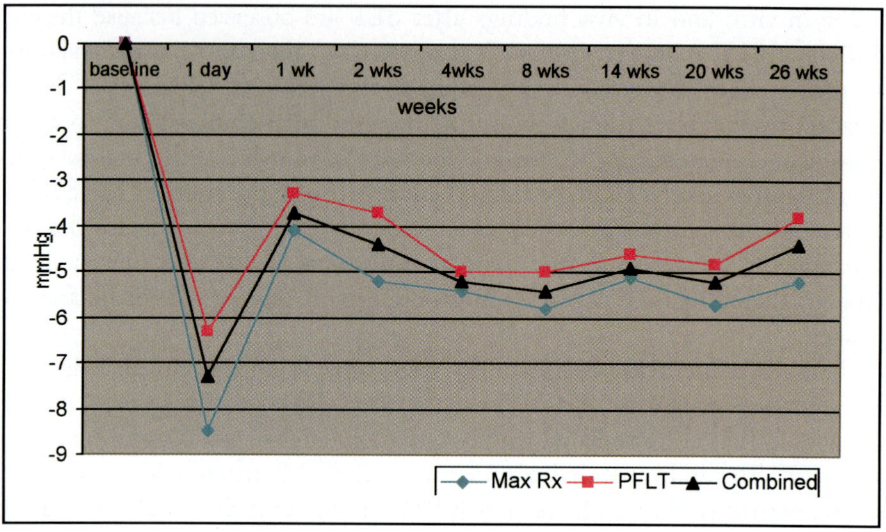

Figure 2: Mean Reduction of Intraocular Pressure in 101 SLT Treated Eyes16 (Max Rx – OAG uncontrolled by maximum medical therapy; PFLT – uncontrolled OAG with a previous history of ALT treatment; Combined – all SLT treated patients in the study).

NY; University of Arizona Health Sciences Center, Tucson, AZ; Kresge Eye Institute, Detroit, MI).[16] Forty five eyes were on maximum tolerated medications (Max Rx group) and 56 eyes had a previous failed argon laser trabeculoplasty (PFLT group). Thirty four of the 45 patients (75.6%) in the Max Rx group, 37 of the 56 patients (66.1%) in the PFLT group responded to treatment with an IOP reduction of at least 3 mmHg up to the 26th week post-SLT. The mean IOP reduction was 5.2 mmHg (20.3%, P<0.0001) for the Max Rx group, 3.8 mmHg (14.7 %; P< 0.001) for the PFLT group, and 4.4 mmHg (17.2%, P<0.001) for both groups combined. **(Figure 2)** The mean number of glaucoma medications decreased from baseline by 1.2 medications. Mild anterior chamber reaction commonly occurred within after SLT irradiation, which usually decreased within 24 hours and was completely resolved by 1 week. The adverse events observed were minimal, transient and were similar to that seen after ALT treatment. An IOP elevation of > 10 mmHg above the immediate preoperative IOP was observed in 7 (5.8%) of the treated eyes. Elevated IOP occurred within 1 to 24 hours after treatment in 5 patients and between 1 to 7 days in the other two patients. (the patients did not receive any prophylactic medications against postoperative IOP spikes). The IOP elevations were managed with topical anti-glaucoma medications and usually resolved within 24 hours. Six patients (5%) experienced eye pain, while another group of 6 patients (5%) developed non-specific conjunctivitis after laser treatment. Other adverse events occurring at less than 1% incidence were blurred vision (0.8%), corneal edema (0.8%), and appearance of a corneal lesion (0.8%) . It should also be stressed that no peripheral anterior synechiae developed in any of the eyes treated with SLT.

What is noteworthy in both studies was that more than 66% of the patients who had a previous failed argon laser trabeculoplasty (PFLT group) had an IOP decrease of 3 mmHg or greater after treatment with SLT. This figure is much higher than those found in literature in which a failed ALT was retreated with another course of ALT where only 32% had an IOP decrease of 3 mmHg or more.[17] This observation was also supported by the findings of Damji & co-workers[10], where they observed that in patients who had a previous history of failed ALT, a significantly greater mean IOP reduction was observed with SLT (6.8 mmHg) as compared to the patients whose eyes were re-treated with another session of ALT (3.6 mmHg).

Investigators in other countries have also demonstrated the safety and efficacy of SLT in lowering the intraocular pressure. **(Table 1)** Kaulen[18] in Germany observed that SLT decreased the mean IOP by 23% in 460 eyes of 328 patients, and the procedure had a 2 year success rate of 80%. The complication rate for SLT in this study was approximately 4.5%, which is much lower than the complication rate of ALT (which may reach up to 34% 2). The most common complications noted were: (1) elevation of IOP in 11 eyes (2.4%) post-operatively (2) significant inflammatory reaction in the anterior chamber without an IOP spike in 7 eyes (1.5%). All the complications were easily treatable with the appropriate eye medications (e.g. steroids).

Table 1: Mean intraocular pressure reduction after Selective Laser Trabeculoplasty (SLT).

	Latina et al.[8] 1998	**Kaulen[18] 2000**	**Latina et al.[16] 2001**	**Hong et al.[19] 1998**	**Damji et al.[10] 1999**
Type of study	Prospective, Clinical	Prospective Clinical	Prospective, Clinical	Randomized, prospective	Randomized, prospective
No. of eyes treated	53 eyes	460 eyes	101 eyes	45 eyes	36 eyes
Duration of follow up	6 _ months	24 months	6 _ months	6 months	6 months
Mean IOP decrease after **SLT**	23.8%	23%	17.2%	30.5%	21.9%
Mean IOP decrease after **ALT**				18.5%	21.3%

Damji et al.[10] in Canada embarked on a prospective randomized clinical trial comparing the effectiveness of SLT and ALT in lowering intraocular pressure in 36 eyes. The IOP lowering effect of both treatment modalities at 6 months were observed to be equivalent ($p = 0.97$), with SLT and ALT lowering IOP by 4.8 mmHg (21.9%) and 4.7 mmHg (21.3%), respectively. Likewise, in a similar study involving 45 Asian eyes, SLT and ALT was noted to have an IOP lowering effect of 30.5% (6.3 mmHg) and 18.5% (3.7 mmHg), respectively.[19]

Method

The procedure is performed similar to a conventional ALT. Pre-operatively, careful gonioscopy should be done to carefully visualize the trabecular meshwork (TM) and plan the treatment area.

Laser Treatment of the Trabecular Meshwork

Pre-operative medications consist of a drop each of brimonidine (0.1%)and topical anesthesia (e.g. proparacaine). A Goldman three-mirror goniolens is then placed on the eye with methylcellulose. The aiming beam is then focused onto the pigmented trabecular meshwork (TM). The 400 µm spot size is large enough to irradiate the entire antero-posterior height of the TM **(Figure 3)**.

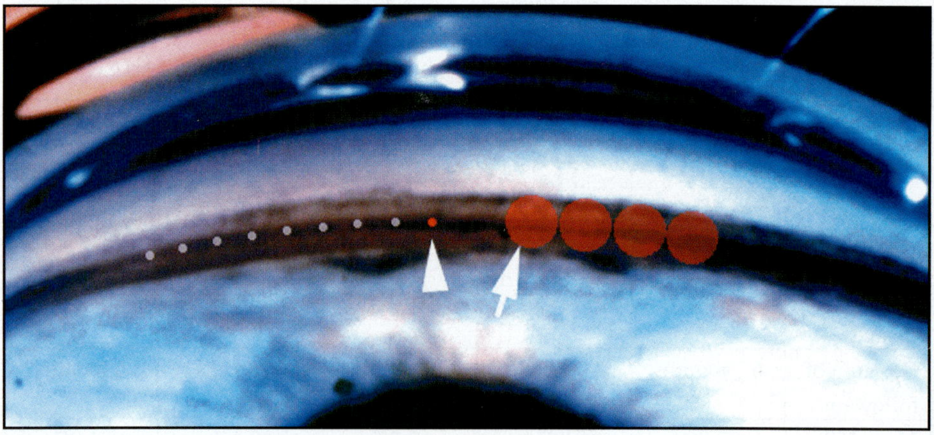

Figure 3: Gonioscopy photograph comparing the spot placements for ALT and SLT. The ALT laser spots (50 um diameter spot size, left arrowhead), are placed in the junction of the anterior one third and posterior two thirds of the TM. On the other hand, the SLT treatment beam (right arrow) measures 400 um and the entire height of the TM can be covered with a single pulse. For both the ALT and the SLT, a total of 50 laser spots are placed to cover approximately 180° of the circumference of the TM ***(Photograph Courtesy of Carl Park, MD).***

The visible endpoints of typical of conventional argon laser trabeculoplasty, such as blanching of the TM or bubble formation within the TM, are not seen with SLT. To determine the optimum energy level for Selective Laser Trabeculoplasty for each eye, the Nd:YAG laser energy is initially set at 0.8 mJ, and then the energy level was increased by 0.1 mJ until the threshold energy for bubble formation is observed. After the threshold energy was identified or if bubble formation is already noted at the initial energy level, the laser energy level is decreased by increments of 0.1 mJ until no bubble formation is observed. This lower energy level is known as the "treatment energy". Treatment is done in single burst mode placing 50 + 5 contiguous, but not overlapping, 400 um laser spots along 180º. Bubble formation is monitored with each pulse. In cases with significant variation in trabecular pigmentation, the pulse energy is decreased if bubble formation occurred as described above.

Postoperative Medications

After laser treatment, prednisolone acetate 1% is administered and continued in the treated eye four times daily for 4 days.

Indications

The indications for treatment with Selective Laser Trabeculoplasty (SLT) are similar to the indications for Argon Laser Trabeculoplasty (ALT). Patients with open angle glaucoma who are candidates for conventional ALT can be considered for SLT. In addition, SLT can be a useful treatment alternative in the following subset of patients:

1. Patients who have a history of failed ALT (either 180º or 360º) will respond well with SLT, thus, offering an alternative to patients who would have otherwise undergone incisional surgery.

2. Patients who are poorly compliant or have problems obtaining or intolerant to their glaucoma medications. This treatment option is also reasonable alternative to medications in patients who have a history of poor "follow up" due to personality, economic, or transportation reasons.

3. Because of the non-destructive and potentially repeatable properties of SLT, this treatment modality may be used as a first line treatment for open angle glaucoma. Choosing this treatment option does not affect the success of future surgical procedures. Furthermore, SLT treatment can be repeated a number of times to control the IOP without being concerned about increasing the failure rate of the

procedure. This treatment modality has the potential to delay or obviate the need for additional medications and/or incisional surgery in patients with open angle glaucoma.

4. SLT has also been shown to work well with patients with pigmentary, pseudoexfoliation, and juvenile open angle glaucomas.

SLT is contraindicated in patients with:

1. Inflammatory/ Uveitic Glaucomas
2. Congenital glaucoma
3. Primary or secondary narrow angle glaucoma
4. Any disease process/ malformation which does not permit the visualization of the trabecular meshwork.

Summary

In summary, Selective Laser Trabeculoplasty is a safe and effective treatment modality for lowering the intraocular pressure in patients with open angle glaucoma. The preservation of the trabecular meshwork architecture and the demonstrated efficacy in lowering the IOP makes the SLT a reasonable and safe alternative to argon laser trabeculoplasty. In addition, SLT is a potentially repeatable procedure because of the lack of coagulation damage to the TM and the demonstrated efficacy in patients with previously failed ALT treatment. Furthermore, SLT can be considered as a primary treatment option in patients who cannot tolerate or are non-compliant with their glaucoma medications, while not interfering with the success of future surgery. Due to its non-destructive properties and low complication rate, Selective Laser Trabeculoplasty has the potential to help as an ideal treatment in open angle glaucoma.

Editorial Comment

As advised by Dr. Mark Latina, one of the world experts in glaucoma, it is most important to keep using the same medication for glaucoma previously used before the laser treatment. In addition, this therapy is supplemented with anti-inflammatory topical steroids during the first week following SLT. This is because the major complication of SLT is an elevation of the intraocular pressure after treatment. This occurs in about 20% of the cases but it can be prevented.

Samuel Boyd, MD. Editor-in-Chief.

References

1. Wise JB, Witter SL. Argon therapy for open angle glaucoma: a pilot study. Arch Ophthalmol 1979; 97: 319-22.
2. The Glaucoma Laser Trial Research Group. The Glaucoma Laser Trial (GLT) and Glaucoma Laser Trial Follow Up Study: 7. Results. Am J Ophthalmol. 1995; 120: 718-31.
3. Hollo G. Argon and low energy, pulsed Nd:YAG laser trabeculoplasty. A prospective, comparative clinical and morphological study. Acta Ophthalmol Scand 1996 Apr; 74(2):126-31.
4. Melamed S, Pei J, Epstein DL. Short term effects of argon laser trabeculoplasty in monkeys. Arch Opthalmol 1985; 103:1546-52.
5. Van der Zypen E, Fankhauser F. Ultrastructural changes of the trabecular meshwork of the monkey (Macaca speciosa) following irradiation with argon laser light. Graefes Arch Clin Exp Ophthalmol 1984; 221: 249-61.
6. Alexander RA, Grierson I. Morphological effects of argon laser trabeculoplasty upon the glaucomatous human meshwork. Eye 1989; 3:719-26.
7. Latina M, Park C. Selective Targeting of Trabecular Meshwork Cells: In Vitro Studies of Pulse and Continuous Laser Interactions. Exp Eye Res 1995; 60, 359-72.
8. Latina MA, Sibayan S. 1996; In vivo selective targeting of trabecular meshwork cells by irradiation: a potential treatment for glaucoma results (Abstract). Invest Ophthalmol Vis Sci 1996; 37 (3): S408.
9. Kramer TR, Noecker RJ. Comparison of the Morphologic Changes after Selective Laser Trabeculoplasty and Argon Laser Trabeculoplasty in Human Eye Bank Eyes. Ophthalmology 2001 April; 108 (4):773-80.
10. Damji KF, Shah KC, Rock WJ et al. Selective laser trabeculoplasty vs. argon laser trabeculoplasty: A prospective randomized clinical trial. Br J Ophthalmol 1999 Jun;83(6): 718-22.
11. Dueker DK, Norberg M, Johnson DH, et al. Stimulation of cell division by argon and Nd: YAG laser trabeculoplasty in cynomolgous monkeys. Invest Ophthalmol Vis Sci 1990; 31: 115-24.
12. Bylysma SS, Samples JR, Acott TS, Van Buskirk EM. Trabecular cell division after argon laser trabeculoplasty. Arch Ophthalmol 1988;106:544-7.
13. Alvarado JA. Mechanical and Biochemical Comparison of ALT and SLT. Ocular Surgery News 2000 March, 7-10.
14. Alvarado JA, Murphy CG. Outflow obstruction in pigmentary and primary open angle glaucoma. Arch Ophthalmol. 1992; 110: 1769-78
15. Latina MA, Sibayan SA, Shin DH et al. Q-switched 532-nm Nd:YAG laser trabeculoplasty (selective laser trabeculoplasty): A multi-center, pilot, clinical study. Ophthalmology 1998 Nov;105(11):2082-8.
16. Latina MA, Tumbocon JA, Noecker RJ et al. Selective laser trabeculoplasty (SLT): The United States prospective multicenter clinical trial results (Abstract). Invest Ophthalmol Vis Sci 2001; 42 (4): S546.
17. Richter CU, Shingleton BJ, Bellows AR et al. Re-treatment with argon laser trabeculoplasty. Ophthalmology 1987; 94:1085-9.
18. Kaulen P. International Clinical Experience with SLT. Ocular Surgery News 2000 March 17-19.
19. Unpublished Study, presented at the 1998 American Academy of Ophthalmology Annual Meeting; Hong YJ, Lee YG et al.

2 The Trabeculectomy Procedure

Maurice Luntz, MD, FACS

Indications

Increasing evidence supports the concept that poorly tolerated maximum medical therapy or medical therapy that does not reduce IOP to appropriate levels (target pressure) no longer has a legitimate role in the management of uncomplicated open-angle glaucoma.

There is a fairly strong tendency to consider surgery earlier than we have had in the past. There are several reasons for this:

1) evidence based on prospective, randomized studies with a mean follow-up of 4.6 years reveals that loss of visual field in patients under medical therapy occur mostly in the first two years after diagnosis while the medical treatment was being modified or until surgery was resorted to in order to aim at achieving the adequate target pressure.[1] (These findings do not reflect negatively on the benefits of medical therapy. The latter have been substantiated through the years. They do reflect negatively on the judgment of many physicians who maintain patients with medical therapy even though the right "target pressure" has not been achieved and hesitate to take the next step, either laser trabeculoplasty or incisional surgery, during long periods in which the patient is maintained at suboptimal pressure levels - *Editors*).

2) Another significant finding in Jay and Allan's studies is that once there is significant field loss, it becomes more difficult to preserve the remaining fields. When adequate control of intraocular pressure was achieved, however, the reduction in visual fields remained the same in the two groups studied, that is, those treated only with medical therapy vs primary trabeculectomy. However, those with already extensive field loss continued to lose fields slowly despite "normal" intraocular pressures but remained stationary in those with little field loss.

These conclusions reveal the importance of achieving the adequate "target pressure" for each individual patient and not to be misled with a false sense of security, as emphasized by Al Sommer[2]. They also explain why we have patients with advanced visual field loss who continue losing fields even though we operate on them successfully.

These findings are reinforced by the studies made at Moorfields in London by Hitchings and Migdal comparing primary surgery with conventional treatment for primary open angle glaucoma. They have demonstrated the importance for visual field preservation of reaching a Target Pressure in the mid teens. These target pressures can be achieved with primary surgery without the use of antifibrotic agents (antimetabolites) and also with medical therapy. The right management of medical treatment is fundamental for success. Any delay in so doing may increase the risk of visual field loss.

The application of topical medications that contain the preservative benzalkonium chloride may induce chronic episcleral inflammation and perhaps affect surgical results after years of using these medications.

When to Operate

Regarding the fundamental question of how to proceed, and when to perform incisional surgery, trabeculectomy is not the primary choice on a newly diagnosed case of glaucoma. The initial approach is always to try medical therapy and follow the patient very closely and over a period of a few months. When we are not satisfied with the level of pressure control and especially when there are changes in the functional status of the eye and maximum therapy, then we decide on laser trabeculoplasty or incisional surgery for better control, depending on the disc changes and field loss, and the presence of various risk factors including systemic diseases.

If there is a threat to central vision we should not wait and must proceed surgically. If the "target pressure" for that patient is not reached and maintained (diurnal pressure checks) with maximum tolerated medication, then ALT is immediately indicated. If this too fails to reach the "target pressure" within a few weeks then a filtering operation is necessary. The danger for the patient is for the ophthalmologist to maintain him/her on a therapy that is not reaching the target pressure for that patient. Indecision or a false sense of security on the part of the physician who maintains the patient on suboptimal levels of intraocular pressure is one of the main factors for continued loss of function. Hitchings[3] has emphasized that an eye which deteriorates at a pressure of 18mm Hg is unlikely to slow its rate of decline if treatment only reduces the intraocular pressure to 16mm Hg. The target pressure needs to be lowered substantially if continued field loss occurs. This point is well demonstrated by many studies in the literature -- for example, Sommer, A.[4] , in the AJO, 1989, 107: 186-8, concluded that elevated IOP produces optic nerve damage, and that the risk of optic nerve damage increases with increased IOP, even when IOP is under 21mm Hg. There is also the study of Pohjanpelto, P.E., Palva[5] , J., Acta. Ophthal., 1974, 52:194-200, who, in a five-year follow-up of patients, concluded that there was visual field progression over the five-year period in 6% of patients who had a moderately increased IOP, in 28-36% of patients with IOP greater than 30mm Hg, and in 57% of patients with IOP of 40mm Hg or more. Another study to Roth, S.M., Spaeth, G.L., Steinmann, W.C., Poryzees, E.M., Starita, R.J., in Invest. Ophthal. Vis Sci. (Suppl.), 1988, 87:519-25, in an eight-year follow-up of patients, these authors concluded that if IOP averaged 19.3mm Hg 58% of patients showed a progression of visual field loss, and if IOP averaged 14.4mm Hg only 6% showed progression of visual field loss. Hence, the ideal IOP in patients with glaucoma should be 15mm Hg or less.

There is also a tendency for earlier surgical management of glaucoma based on studies that show better stability of IOP control with surgery -- e.g., Odberg, T., in Acta. Ophthal. (Suppl.), 1987, 182:27-29, in a five to 18-year follow-up, concluded that visual fields showed twice the stability in surgically treated eyes compared to medically treated eyes.

Kolker, A.E., in Trans. Am Ophthal. Soc., 1977, 75:539-55, in a four-year follow-up, concluded that visual field loss was progressive in 59% of medically treated patients compared to 23% of surgically treated patients in their study. These studies emphasize that patients with glaucoma and visual field loss should be maintained with IOP in the low teens to put the patient at the lowest possible risk of progressive visual field loss.

Another factor determining a shift to an earlier surgical treatment for glaucoma, or, in some countries, performing surgery as the primary treatment of chronic open-angle glaucoma, is the cost factor. Maintaining patients on long-term medical therapy is expensive and in many poorer countries not feasible.

FILTERING OPERATIONS
THE CLASSIC TRABECULECTOMY PROCEDURE

Trabeculectomy With Fornix Based Flap

The most frequently performed operation for open angle glaucoma is trabeculectomy.[1] Maurice Luntz, M.D., popularized the trabeculectomy with fornix based conjunctival flap and tightly sutured scleral flap[2] years ago by demonstrating its advantages and effectiveness in different people races **(Figure 1)**.[3] This procedure is a keratectomy and trabeculectomy extending to the scleral spur and covered by a half-thickness scleral flap (Figure 6) which is tightly sutured back into place and can be used in standard open angle glaucoma cases as well as in eyes with glaucoma and cataract.

Advantages of Fornix-Based Flap Trabeculectomy

The advantages of this technique over the limbus based flap trabeculectomy are as follows:

1) There is better exposure and visualization of the operating field. Dissection of the scleral flap well into the cornea is facilitated (Figures 6, 10,11). This insures a trabeculectomy well in front of the root of the iris and ciliary body and reduces the possibility of hypertrophic ciliary body pigment or iris adhesions obstructing the trabeculectomy opening.

2) The procedure is technically easier than dissecting a limbus based flap, especially when operating in an area of scarred conjunctiva, from either previous trauma or surgery.

3) The possibility of damaging the conjunctival flap during dissection, especially button-holing the flap, is eliminated.

4) The conjunctival flap adheres to and scars at the limbus. The subconjunctival bleb that results is pushed posteriorly producing a diffuse, well vascularized thicker-walled bleb in the upper half of the conjunctiva. There is little possibility of developing a thin, avascular bleb anteriorly placed and overhanging the cornea.

5) The scleral flap is sutured back into place. The flap prevents excessive aqueous humor filtration and maintains the anterior chamber postoperatively.

6) The same technique can be effectively used for combined cataract surgery and trabeculectomy with all its advantages. The risk of shallow or absent anterior chamber postoperatively is considerably less with this method.

Surgical Technique

Conjunctival Flap

A fornix based conjunctival flap 7 mm long is fashioned at the limbus **(Figure 1)**. The conjunctiva is dissected back in a natural surgical plane between the conjunctiva, episclera and sclera. Any bleeding points on the conjunctiva or sclera are dealt with at this stage.

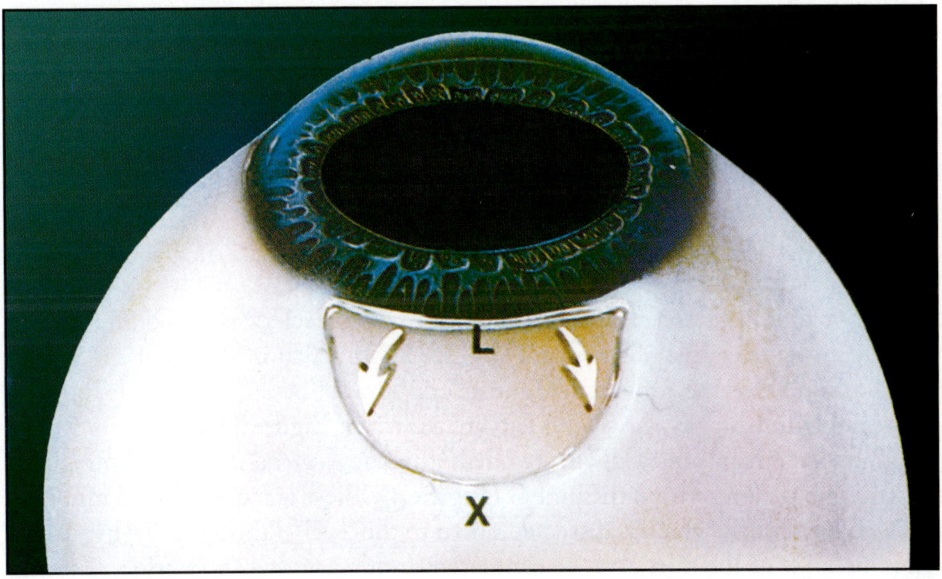

Figure 1: Trabeculectomy with Fornix Based Flap: A fornix based flap (X) is dissected at the limbus (L) for a length of 7 mm. The conjunctiva is dissected back in a plane between the conjunctiva, episclera and sclera up to the initial fornix based incision (X), 4 mm behind the limbus. (Art from Jaypee Highlights Medical Publishers, Inc.)

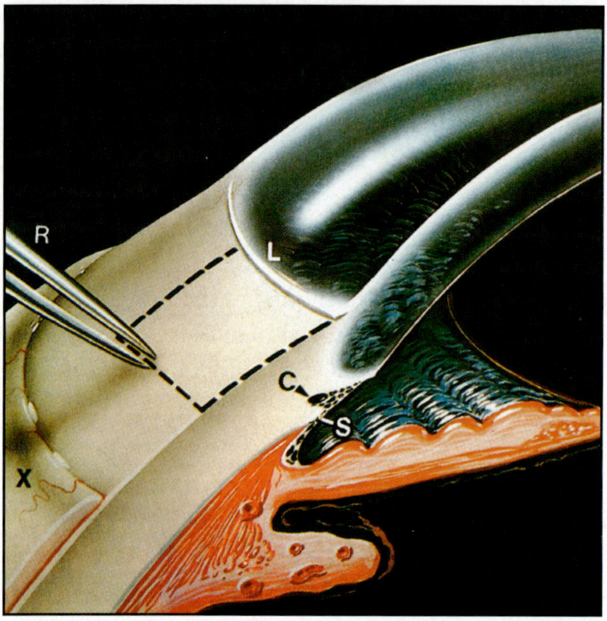

Figure 2: Trabeculectomy with Fornix Based Flap - Outlining the Scleral Flap - Anatomical Relations with Angle Structures: The scleral surface is cleaned and a 3 mm x 3 mm scleral flap hinged at the limbus (L) is outlined with cautery (R), (dotted line). Fornix based conjunctival flap (X). The Canal of Schlemm (C) is shown lying over the trabeculum and scleral spur, (S). (Art from Jaypee Highlights Medical Publishers, Inc.)

Dissection Scleral Flap

The scleral surface is cleaned and a 3 mm x 3 mm scleral flap is outlined with cautery in the bare area of the sclera **(Figure 2)**. This flap is hinged at the limbus which insures that the conjunctival and scleral suture lines are separated. The anatomical relationships of the scleral flap are shown in **Figure 3 (A-B)**.

The scleral flap is incised with two half-thickness scleral incisions 3 mm apart extending back 3 mm from the limbus **(Figure 4)**. These are joined by a 3 mm long incision posteriorly which is dissected down to the level of the choroid **(Figure 5)**. The thickness of the sclera can be estimated from the posterior incision, allowing accurate dissection of scleral flaps of varying thickness. The thickness chosen for the scleral flap depends on the pathology and the prognosis for surgery. Ideally, the flap should be half the scleral thickness which permits adequate aqueous filtration but avoids the possibility of an excessively thin scleral flap becoming staphylomatous. The dissection of the scleral flap is commenced from the posterior incision at the desired thickness and, staying in the same surgical plane, it is carried forward into the cornea to just within the surgical limbus **(Figures 5 and 6)**.

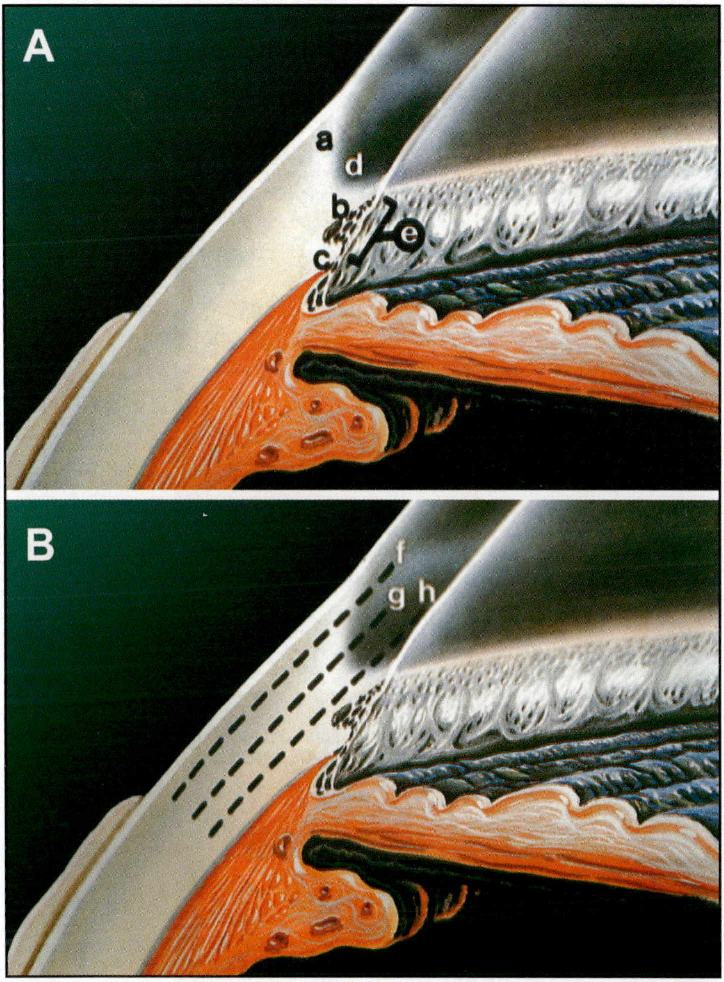

Figure 3A-B: Anatomical Relationships for the Scleral Flap in Trabeculectomy: These anatomical relationships are of great value as a guide to localize the trabeculectomy opening in the right place and in performing the desired-thickness scleral flap. Fig. (A) Near the corneo-scleral junction, the three finger-like anterior digitations of the sclera are noted (a), (b) and (c). (c) is the scleral spur. The corneal border in the form of a wedge is indicated at (d). The Canal of Schlemm and trabeculum are shown at (e). Fig. (B) The scleral flap for trabeculectomy can vary in thickness, as follows, in relation to the anatomical structures shown in Fig. (A); (f) Very thin scleral flap entering the cornea above and anterior to the blunt tip of the corneal wedge. This type of flap is undesirable. (g) Half thickness scleral flap penetrating corneal tissue approximately at the vertex of the corneal wedge. This is the most desirable flap. (h) Extremely thick scleral flap penetrating the cornea below and a little advanced to the vertex of the corneal wedge. This flap is also undesirable. (Art from Jaypee Highlights Medical Publishers, Inc.)

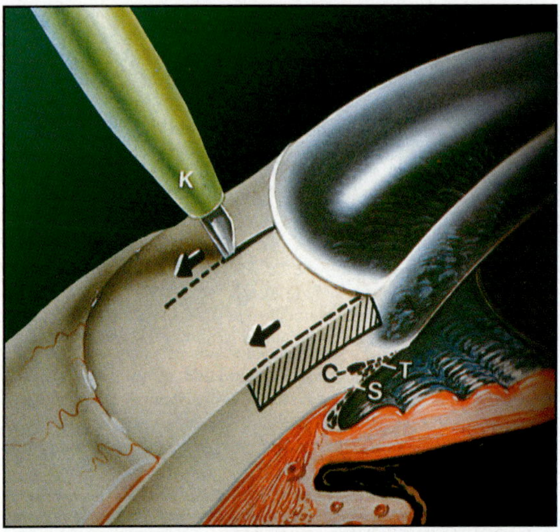

Figure 4: Trabeculectomy with Fornix Based Flap - Incising the Scleral Flap. The scleral flap is incised with two half-thickness incisions radially. Scleral knife (K). The depth of these incisions is denoted by the cross-hatched area on the scleral cross section. The Canal of Schlemm (C) is indicated lying over the trabeculum (T) and scleral spur, (S). (Art from Jaypee Highlights Medical Publishers, Inc.)

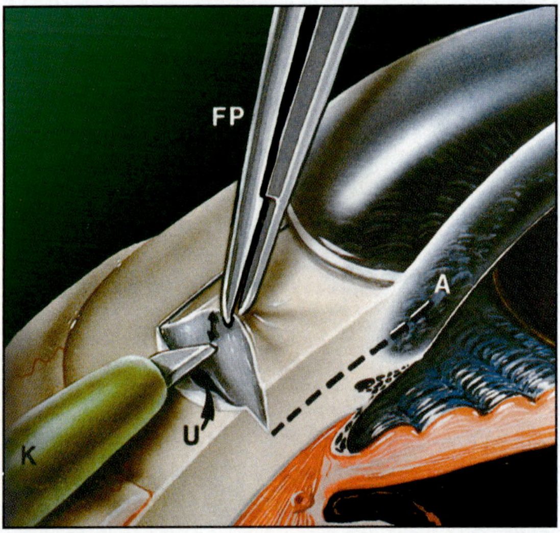

Figure 5: Trabeculectomy with Fornix Flap-Beginning the Scleral Flap Dissection. The two radial incisions are joined posteriorly with a scleral incision extending down to the level of the choroid at one spot, (U). With the full thickness of the sclera observable by lifting this posterior incision with forceps (FP), the desired thickness for the scleral flap is determined. This is predetermined by performing a half-thickness (small double arrows) scleral flap. With the knife (K), dissection of the scleral flap is commenced. Staying in the same surgical plane, the dissection is carried forward (along the dotted line) into the cornea at point (A). (Art from Jaypee Highlights Medical Publishers, Inc.)

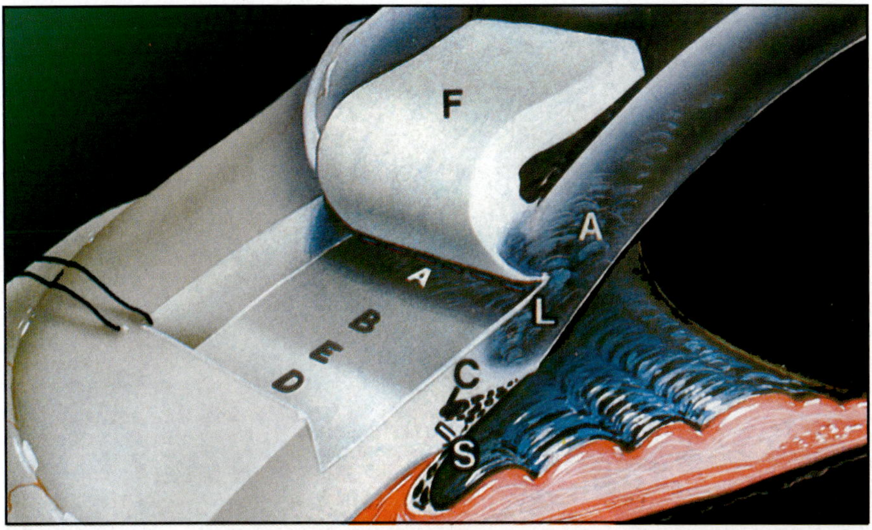

Figure 6: Trabeculectomy Gonioscopic View - Relationships of Internal Structures to External Landmarks. Relationships to external landmarks seen in Fig. 7 include (A) - transparent cornea; (B) - trabeculum (gray band); (D) - white opaque sclera. The junction of the trabeculum gray band (B) with the white opaque sclera (D) denotes the deeper scleral spur (S) which is seen as (E) externally. Scleral flap (F), Canal of Schlemm (C). The external limbus is denoted as a dotted line (L) in clear cornea, (A). (Art from Jaypee Highlights Medical Publishers, Inc.)

Under the scleral flap, the salient external landmarks are easily recognized in the undissected scleral portion **(Figure 6)** anteriorly, transparent, deep corneal tissue; behind this, a gray band of parallel-layered tissue which overlies the trabecular meshwork and merges into white, opaque sclera with crisscrossing fibers. At the junction of the gray trabecular band and the sclera is the scleral spur and Schlemm canal. This external landmark for the scleral spur (the junction of the posterior border of the trabeculum band and the sclera) is by far the most important surgical landmark. It indicates the site of the scleral spur and thus the posterior limit of the corneo-trabecular tissue removed in a trabeculectomy and it also indicates the approximate location of the Canal of Schlemm.

The relationship of the internal structures to the external landmarks involved in a trabeculectomy operation are shown in a gonioscopic view in **Figure 7**.

Schlemm's canal is anatomically related to the scleral spur. In some eyes, it is situated just anterior to the scleral spur and is then found histologically in the trabeculectomy specimen. In others, it lies at or behind the scleral spur. In the former case, it is difficult to identify histologically in the trabeculectomy specimen; in the latter case, it is not in the trabeculectomy specimen. In **Figure 7** Schlemm's canal is indicated lying in front of the scleral spur.

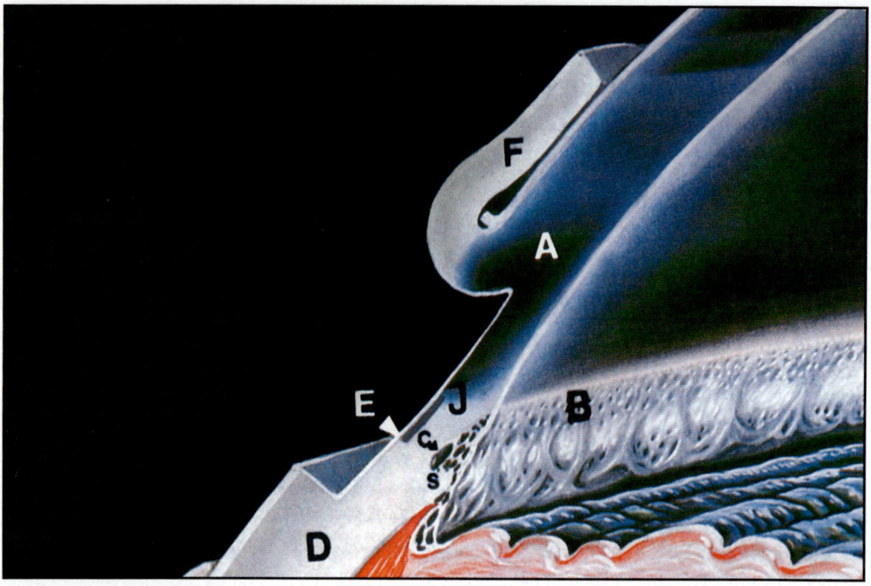

Figure 7: Trabeculectomy Surgical and Anatomical Landmarks: The half-thickness scleral flap (F) is reflected. (A) - transparent cornea; (B) - gray band (trabeculum); (D) - white opaque sclera. The junction of the gray band (B) and the sclera (D) denotes the external location (E) of the deeper scleral spur (S). Schlemm's Canal (C) is anatomically related to the scleral spur (S). Corneo-scleral junction (J). (Art from Jaypee Highlights Medical Publishers, Inc.)

Trabeculectomy Opening

The next step is to outline a 2 mm x 2 mm square of cornea and trabeculum in the undissected cornea and sclera deep to the scleral flap extending anteriorly from the limbus back to the scleral spur and hinged at the scleral spur, incising to 1/2 the depth of this tissue **(Figure 8)**. The anterior incision is made at the surgical limbus which is well into the deeper layers of the cornea **(Figure 8)**. On postoperative gonioscopy, the trabeculectomy opening can be seen to extend well into the posterior corneal surface and well clear of the iris (Figure 13). The side incisions extend back to the scleral spur. No posterior incision is made at this time. With the internal flap outlined, the anterior incision is dissected through Descemet's membrane into the anterior chamber which is not lost at this stage as iris will plug the incision. A Vannas scissors is carefully introduced and the anterior incision completed still without losing the anterior chamber. This is extended along the sides, cutting back to the external landmark for the scleral spur **(Figure 9)**. The flap is removed by a posterior incision just in front of the scleral spur, visualizing the scleral spur by rotating the flap posteriorly **(Figures 10, 11, 12).**

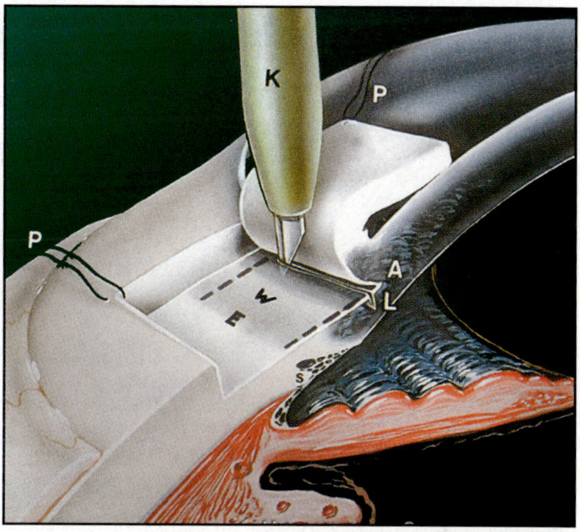

Figure 8: Trabeculectomy with Fornix Based Flap - Outlining the Tissue Window to be Removed. A 2 mm x 2 mm square cornea and trabeculum is outlined with a sharp knife (K). This tissue to be removed (W) extends anteriorly from the surgical limbus (L), which is well into the deep layers of the cornea (A), posteriorly to the scleral spur (S), indicated by the posterior border of the gray band (E). This window is incised one half the depth of this tissue, making an anterior cut along the limbus and two side cuts each extending posteriorly to the external landmark for the scleral spur, (E). No posterior incision is made at this stage. 10-0 nylon sutures (P) should be pre-placed at the posterior corners of the scleral flap and the scleral bed and moved out of the way. (Art from Jaypee Highlights Medical Publishers, Inc.)

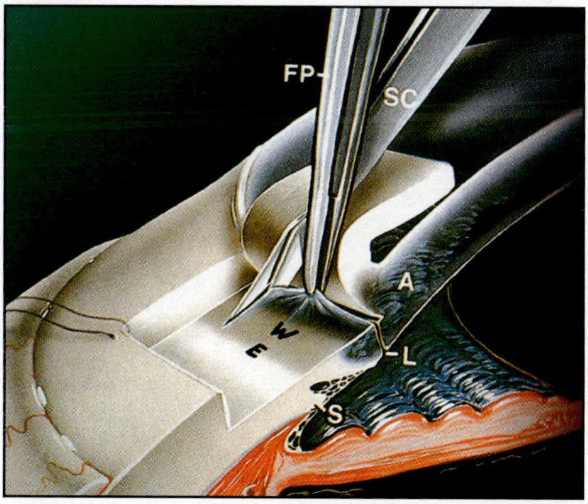

Figure 9: Trabeculectomy with Fornix Based Flap - Extending the Window Along the Sides. With the knife, the anterior incision at the limbus (L) which is in clear cornea (A), has been dissected through Descemet's membrane into the anterior chamber. Using Vannas scissors (SC) the anterior incision is completed. The radial incisions (shown here) are made through the trabeculum (W) to the external landmark (E) representing the scleral spur (S). Forceps, (FP). (Art from Jaypee Highlights Medical Publishers, Inc.)

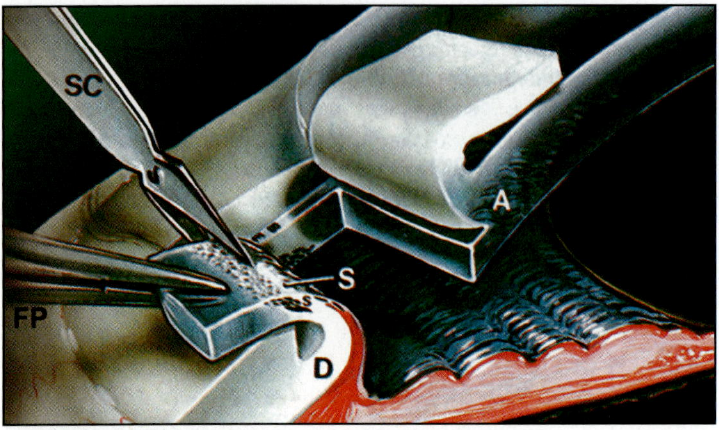

Figure 10: Completing the Trabeculectomy Opening. A posterior incision of the trabeculectomy flap is made just in front of the scleral spur (S) using Vannas scissors, (SC). This completes the excision of the flap of Trabeculum and cornea. The scleral spur, (S), is visualized by rotating the Trabeculectomy flap posteriorly with forceps (FP) so that one is looking directly at the scleral spur (S). Junction of gray band (B) and white opaque sclera (D) is noted at (E), which is the external landmark for the scleral spur. Clear cornea (A). Externally, the gray band (B) reveals the location of the deeper trabeculum. (Art from Jaypee Highlights Medical Publishers, Inc.)

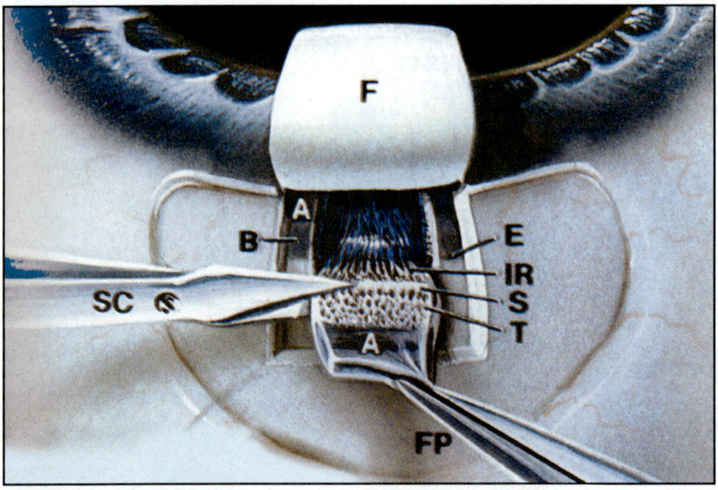

Figure 11: Trabeculectomy with Fornix Based Flap - Removing the Trabecular Window - Surgeon's View. This is a surgeon's view of the final incision to remove the trabecular window, as seen in Fig. 10. It also reveals the surgeon's view of the structures most important to proper trabeculectomy. The Trabeculectomy flap which is being excised has been hinged backwards exposing its deep surface to the surgeon's view. The Vannas scissors (SC), make the final cut just in front of the scleral spur (S), on the trabecular tissue which is here being reflected back with forceps (FP). The scleral spur is localized externally (E) by the junction of white sclera and gray band (B). Scleral flap (F). Clear cornea (A). Iris (I). Iris root (IR). Trabeculum (T). (Art from Jaypee Highlights Medical Publishers, Inc.)

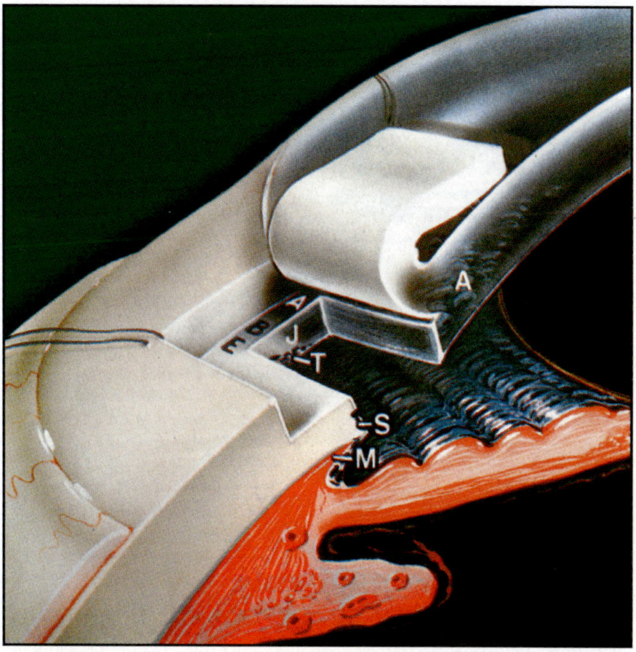

Figure 12: Exposure of Vital Structures Through Trabeculectomy. Final location of the "window" in relation to the trabecular structures. Insertion of ciliary muscle (M) remains intact at the scleral spur (S). Canal of Schlemm not visible in this view. It is placed just anterior to the scleral spur and has been partially removed with the excised cornea and trabeculum. Trabeculum (T) along the radial wall of the "window". Junction of sclera and cornea, (J). Clear cornea (A).

Adjacent to the radial wall of the excised "window" is an unexcised portion of the bed of the lamellar scleral flap which demonstrates the external landmarks for these internal structures. Clear cornea (A), gray band which is the external landmark for the trabeculum (B). External landmark for scleral spur (E). The scleral spur (S) lies in relationship to "E".

On the opposite side of the "window", the radial wall has been removed. Anterior incision lies in clear cornea. Posterior incision lies immediately in front of scleral spur. A portion of the posterior trabeculum in the sclera just behind this posterior incision of the "window". This good exposure is made possible with a fornix based conjunctival flap. (Art from Jaypee Highlights Medical Publishers, Inc.)

An iridectomy is now made. It is imperative that the iridectomy be wider than the trabeculectomy opening so that iris pillars are not pushed into this opening postoperatively **(Figure 13).** This is achieved by grasping the iris with forceps, moving it to the left and commencing an iridectomy incision with scissors from the right side **(Figure 13)**. As this incision approaches the midway point of the iris, the iris is moved across to the right and put on stretch and the incision is completed toward the left side.

As the iridectomy is completed, the anterior chamber may be lost and can be maintained with air or viscoelastics.

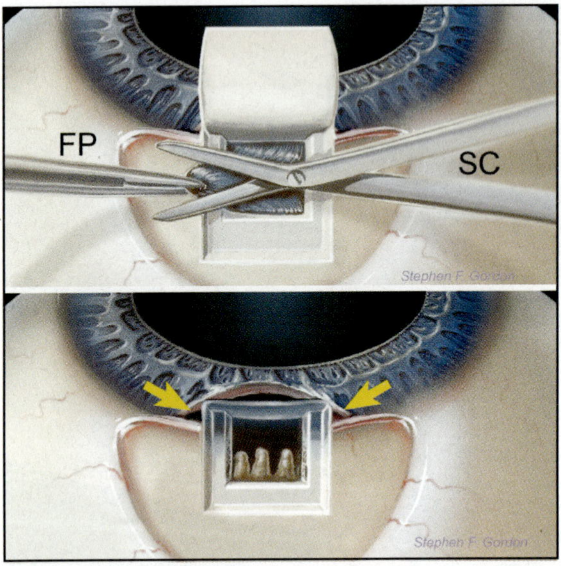

Figure 13: Trabeculectomy with Fornix Based Flap - Performing the Iridectomy. An iridectomy is performed through the excised "window" of cornea and trabeculum. The iridectomy must be wider than the trabeculectomy opening so that iris pillars are not pushed into this opening postoperatively. (Above): the iris is first grasped with a forceps (FP) and pulled to the left while cutting with a scissors from the right side (SC). (Below): the iridectomy boundaries, indicated at the arrows, go beyond the edges of the trabeculectomy opening. (Art from Jaypee Highlights Medical Publishers, Inc.)

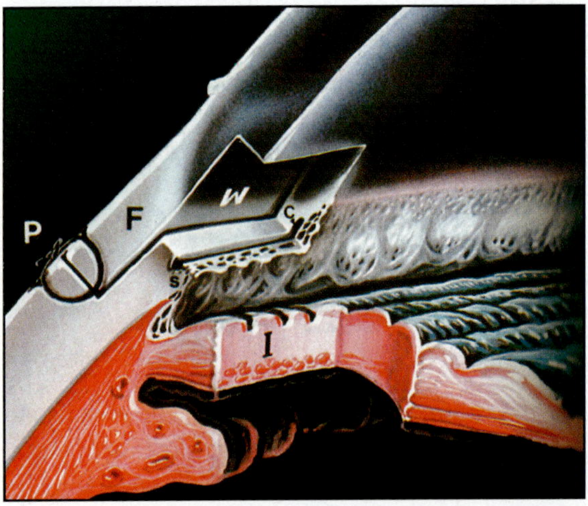

Figure 14: Trabeculectomy with Fornix Based Flap - Final Configuration - Inner View. This internal cross-section view reveals the final configuration once the external partial-thickness scleral flap (F) is repositioned into its scleral bed and the 10-0 nylon sutures (P) at the posterior corners of the flap are tied. Iridectomy is at (I). Trabeculectomy window is at (W). The Canal of Schlemm (C) is indicated lying anterior to the scleral spur (S) and has, therefore, been included in the corneo-trabeculectomy excision. (Art from Jaypee Highlights Medical Publishers, Inc.)

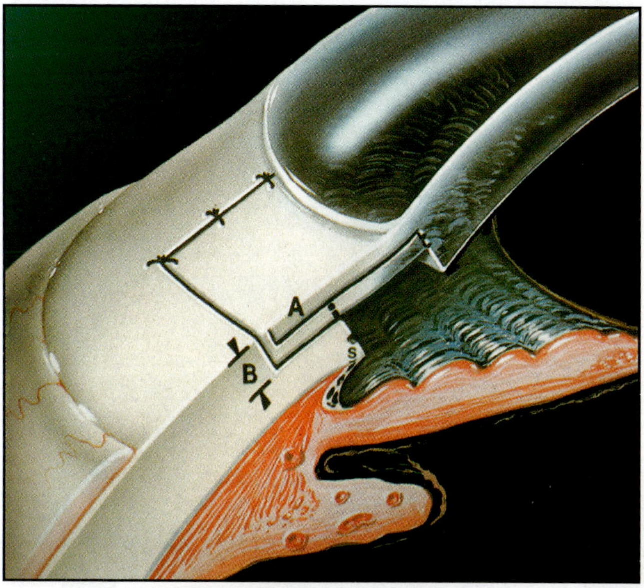

Figure 15: Trabeculectomy - Final Configuration - Surgeon's View. The scleral flap is sutured with six 10-0 nylon sutures (see also Fig.16). These sutures may be removed later with the argon laser applied through the conjunctiva if increased flow of aqueous is desired (Laser Suture Lysis). In (B) is shown the recommended 1/2 thickness of the scleral flap. In (A) is shown a thinner flap which is not recommended. (Art from Jaypee Highlights Medical Publishers, Inc.)

Suturing Lamellar Scleral Flap

The conjunctiva is rotated anteriorly to the limbus and sutured with two 10-0 nylon sutures placed through the conjunctiva and sclera at each end of the conjunctival flap, pulling the conjunctival edge taut along the limbus **(Figure 16)**.

Balanced salt solution is injected under the conjunctival flap to lift it from the sclera. The patient leaves the operating table with an intact anterior chamber and a bleb at the site of the trabeculectomy. If the surgeon decides to use viscoelastics in the anterior chamber during the procedure, it should be removed at the end of the operation to avoid elevation of the intraocular pressure postoperatively.

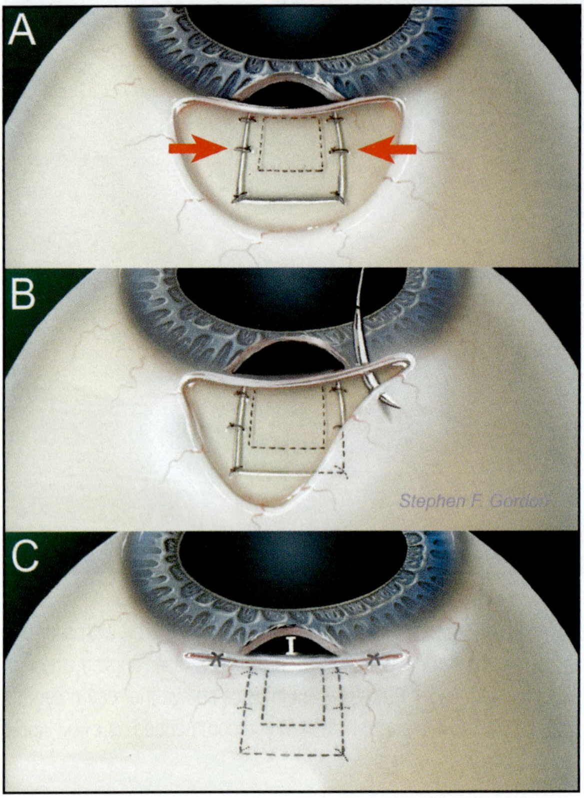

Figure 16: Trabeculectomy with Fornix Based Flap - Conjunctival Closure. These series of steps demonstrate the technique of conjunctival closure. (A) Additional 10-0 nylon sutures have been added to the now closed partial-thickness scleral flap, one pair (arrows) midway between the anterior and posterior ends of the radial flap incisions. Another pair of sutures have been added near the limbus. The 2 x 2 mm trabeculectomy "window" is shown as a dotted line, located deep to the external scleral flap. (B) The conjunctiva is rotated anteriorly to the limbus and sutured with two 10-0 nylon sutures, placed at each end of the conjunctival flap as shown and anchored in superficial lamellae of sclera. (C) The final configuration demonstrates the conjunctival flap sutured to the sclera. Iridectomy located at (I). (Art from Jaypee Highlights Medical Publishers, Inc.)

Trabeculectomy With Limbus Based Flap

Surgical Technique

The technique for this commonly performed procedure is shown in **Figures 17, 18, 19, 20, 21**. This method has the slight disadvantage of being technically somewhat more difficult than when dissecting a fornix based flap, especially when operating in an area of scarred conjunctiva. There is also the possibility of button-holing the flap.

The actual trabeculectomy, cutting out about a one by two millimeter flap of the trabecular meshwork, may be done with a sharp blade, as shown previously for the fornix based conjunctival flap technique, **(Figures 1 through 16)** or with a trephine, as shown here in **Figures 18** through **21**. The trabeculectomy block should be removed anterior to the scleral spur. By leaving the scleral spur undisturbed, there is far less bleeding and you avoid a cyclodialysis effect that cuts down filtration through the cleft in the early postoperative period.

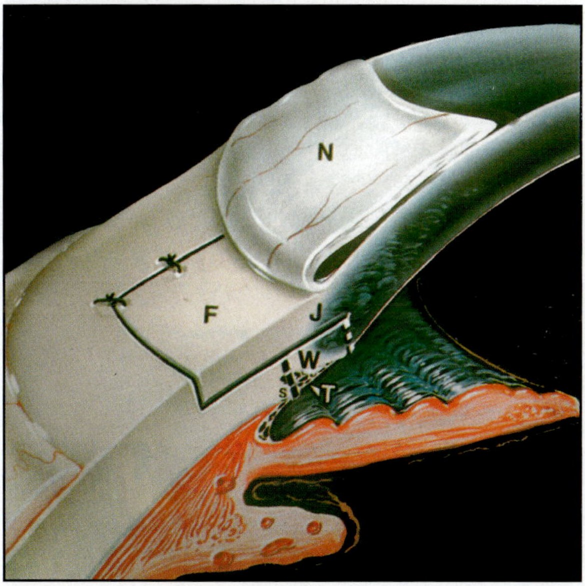

Figure 17: Trabeculectomy With a Limbus Based Flap - Anatomical Relationships. The trabeculectomy "window" (W) is shown here in place but this is the block of tissue actually removed. A half thickness scleral flap (F) has been sutured back into place. A limbus based conjunctival flap has been used (N). The Canal of Schlemm has a variable relationship to the scleral spur; it may lie anterior to the spur, at the spur or behind the spur or overlap the spur. Thus the Trabeculectomy "window" may or may not include the Canal of Schlemm depending on the situation of the Canal. In this illustration, the Canal of Schlemm lies behind the scleral spur (S) and trabeculum (T). The corneal-scleral junction is seen in (J). (Art from Jaypee Highlights Medical Publishers, Inc.)

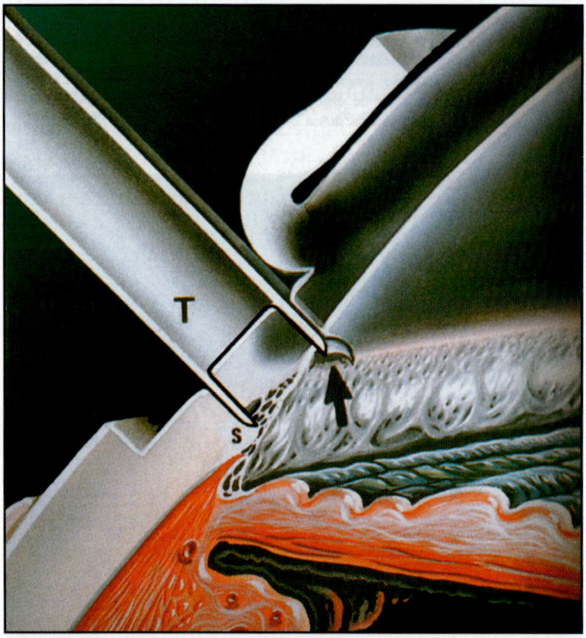

Figure 18: Trabeculectomy With a Limbus Based Flap Performed With Trephine. When using a trephine to perform a trabeculectomy, it is advised to perforate the anterior chamber along the corneal side first rather than 360º all at once. Here the trephine (T) is titled forward. The trephine is seen penetrating (arrow) the anterior chamber along the corneal side first. As soon as aqueous oozes out, the trephine is withdrawn and the operculum is completed with a sharp razor. This is done to carefully inspect, under high magnification, proper localization of the operculum with reference to the scleral spur (S), so as not to excise the spur. (Art from Jaypee Highlights Medical Publishers, Inc.)

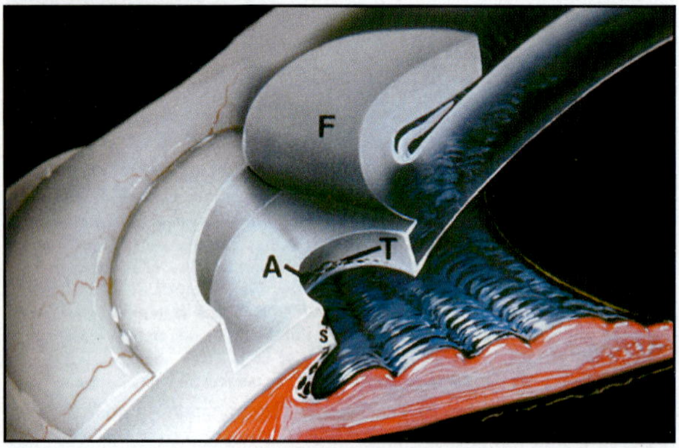

Figure 19: Trabeculectomy With Limbus Based Flap - External Cross Section View – Anatomical Relationships. The trabeculectomy performed with the trephine is complete as seen from the external perspective. The trephined operculum has incorporated a portion of the Canal of Schlemm (A) and the subjacent trabeculum (T). Corneo-scleral lamella (F). The scleral spur (S) lies intact at the posterior edge of the operculum. (Art from Jaypee Highlights Medical Publishers, Inc.)

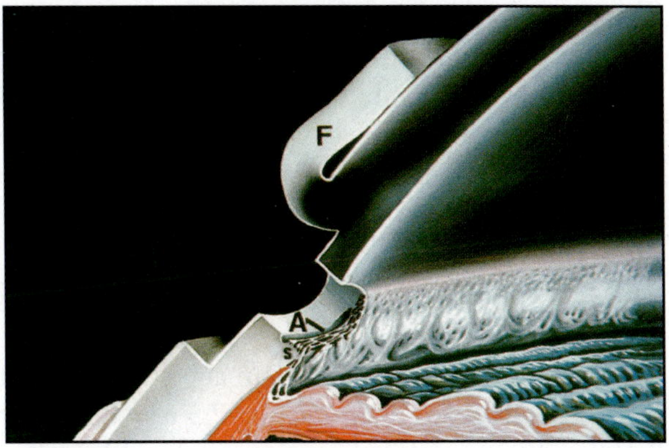

Figure 20: Trabeculectomy With Limbus Based Flap. Gonioscopic Cross Section View. The final removed operculum is shown in relation to the angle structures visible in a gonioscopic view. The partially excised Canal of Schlemm (A) is visible. The area of removed trabeculum is also visible. Intact scleral spur (S). (Art from Jaypee Highlights Medical Publishers, Inc.)

Use of Viscoelastics in Trabeculectomy

Viscoelastics may be injected in the anterior chamber during trabeculectomy to significantly decrease the complication rate. Some surgeons use viscoelastics during glaucoma surgery not only in the anterior chamber but also under the conjunctival flap with the intent to increase the rate of successful postoperative diffuse filtration blebs.

If there is bleeding at the time of excision of the scleral block or iridectomy, then a viscoelastic should be injected immediately. This pushes blood from the anterior chamber out the cleft, raises the intraocular pressure and usually stops the bleeding. The use of viscoelastics does not improve the results of intraocular pressure control nor the percentage of diffuse filtering blebs obtained.

THE TUNNEL SCLERAL INCISION TRABECULECTOMY

Surgical Technique

The Tunnel Scleral Incision Trabeculectomy is Dr. Luntz' preferred technique. All three techniques have essentially the same results when properly done. Which one to perform depends on the individual surgeon's particular inclination.

Maurice Luntz, M.D., F.A.C.S and Abraham Schlossman, M.D. have developed a modified trabeculectomy using a "tunnel" scleral incision based on the type of incision initially utilized in cataract surgery with phacoemulsification.[6]

This tunnel scleral incision trabeculectomy has excellent result, at least comparable to those obtained using the standard trabeculectomy technique originally described by Cairns[7] but, in addition, has one advantage: it considerably simplifies the dissection of the lamellar scleral flap with extremely smooth surfaces. This tunnel incision which is preferred to the standard incision used to be the same incision made for phacoemulsification cataract extraction, so that any surgeon using this latter technique should be familiar with it.

Dissection of the sclera with the crescent knife to make a tunnel is an easier method of dissecting a lamellar scleral flap (which is completed by two radial incisions with Vannas scissors) than the standard method which requires knife dissection of the scleral flap starting 2.5 mm behind the limbus and dissecting to the limbus. The tunnel incision is completed by entering the anterior chamber with a 3.2 mm keratome, an easier technique than dissecting through the deep scleral base into the AC as is done in the standard technique.

The inner surface of the lamellar scleral flap and the surface of the deep scleral base are much smoother with the tunnel incision than can be achieved by dissecting in accordance with the standard method.

Surgical Technique

Conjunctival Flap

A 5 mm wide, fornix-based conjunctival flap is raised at the limbus in the superonasal quadrant. The advantages of a fornix-based conjunctival flap are: 1) the Tenon's fascia is minimally traumatized; 2) there is better exposure of the limbal area; and 3) thinning of the limbal conjunctiva and overhang of the cornea are avoided. With the conjunctival flap pushed posteriorly, hemostasis of exposed sclera is obtained.

Tunnel Incision

Using a crescent knife, an incision is made parallel and 2 mm posterior to the limbus, extending 3 mm in width **(Figure 21)**. The incision is carried down to about one-third of the scleral thickness **(Figure 22)**. The same knife is introduced at the base of this incision and dissects anteriorly toward the limbus **(Figure 22)**, extending into the cornea just anterior to the vascular arcade, forming an intracorneal pocket at about one-third scleral depth with a width of 3 mm. A 3.2 mm keratome is introduced into the scleral pocket and advanced to its anterior edge immediately anterior to the limbal-corneal vessels. The point of the keratome is then depressed and the keratome advanced into the anterior chamber for its full

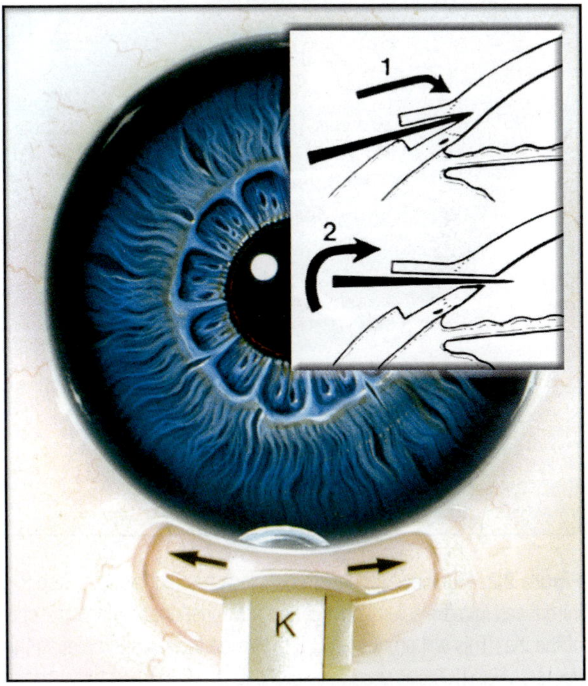

Figure 21: Modified "Tunnel" Trabeculectomy Technique - Step 1 - Conjunctival and Initial Incision. A 5 mm wide, fornix-base conjunctival flap is raised at the limbus in the superonasal quadrant. A Crescent knife (K) then makes an incision 2 mm posterior to and parallel to the limbus extending 3 mm in width. The incision is perpendicular to the sclera and carried down to about 1/3 of the scleral thickness.

This cross section view shows the fornix-based conjunctival flap and the initial incision made with the Crescent knife (K). Notice that this incision is 2mm posterior to the limbus and extends to a depth of 1/3 the thickness of the sclera (arrows - inset).

The Crescent knife (K) is then introduced at the base of the initial incision and dissects anteriorly toward the limbus (arrows), extending into the cornea just anterior to the vascular arcade. This will form an intracorneal pocket at about 1/3 scleral depth and with a width of 3mm. (Art from Jaypee Highlights Medical Publishers, Inc.)

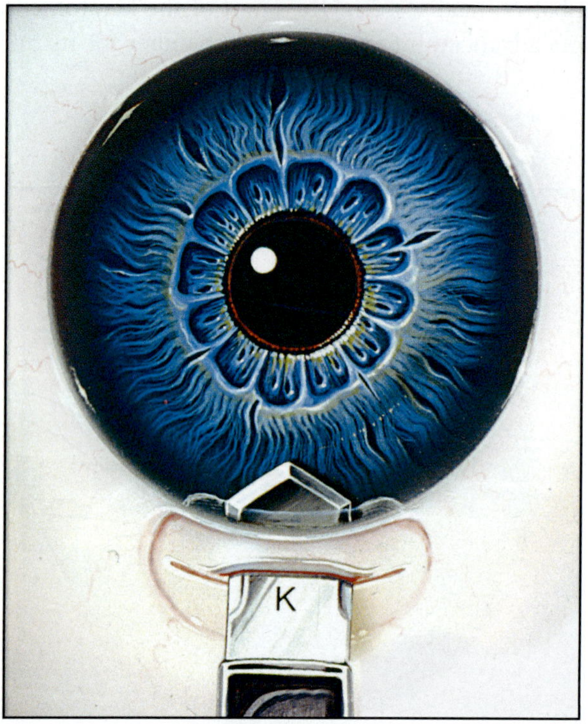

Figure 22: Modified "Tunnel" Trabeculectomy Technique - Step 2 - Tunnel Incision. A 3.2 mm keratome (K), is introduced into the scleral pocket and advanced into the anterior chamber, directed parallel (arrow) to the plane of the iris. This will produce a 3.2 mm wide incision, completing the tunnel incision into the anterior chamber. (Art from Jaypee Highlights Medical Publishers, Inc.)

length, directed parallel to the plane of the iris, producing a 3.2 mm wide incision **(Figure 22)**. This maneuver completes a tunnel incision into the anterior chamber.

Forming the Lamellar Scleral Flap

A Vannas scissors is used to fashion a radial incision at each side of the tunnel **(Figure 23),** producing a 3.2 x 2 mm lamellar scleral flap.

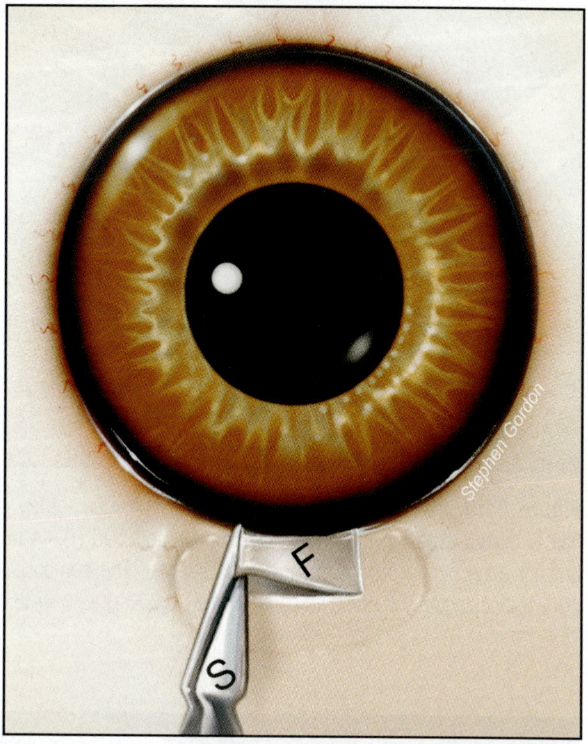

Figure 23: Modified "Tunnel" Trabeculectomy Technique - Step 3 - Lamellar Scleral Flap. A Vannas scissors (S) is used to fashion a radial incision at each side of the tunnel, to form the lamellar scleral flap. The resulting flap (F) is 3.2 mm wide by 2mm antero-posterior. (Art from Jaypee Highlights Medical Publishers, Inc.)

Trabeculectomy

The lamellar scleral flap is raised, exposing the underlying sclerocorneal bed. A Luntz-Dodick punch is advanced to the anterior edge of the sclerocorneal bed **(Figure 24)**, and corneoscleral tissue is punched out until a 2 x 2 mm trabeculectomy opening is fashioned **(Figures 25** and **26)**. An iridectomy is then performed, ensuring that the base of the iridectomy is wider than the trabeculectomy opening **(Figures 25** and **26)**.

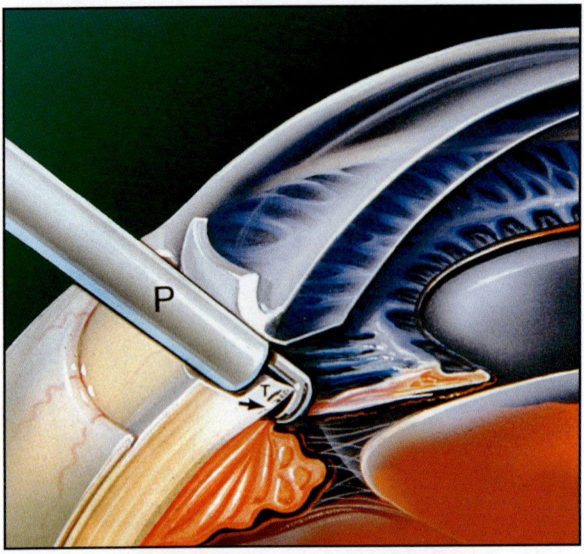

Figure 24: Modified "Tunnel" Trabeculectomy Technique - Step 4 - Trabeculectomy. The lamellar scleral flap is raised, exposing the underlying sclerocorneal bed (T). A Luntz-Dodick punch (P) is advanced to the anterior edge of the sclerocorneal bed as shown. The corneoscleral tissue (arrow) is punched out until a 2 x 2 trabeculectomy opening is made. (Art from Jaypee Highlights Medical Publishers, Inc.)

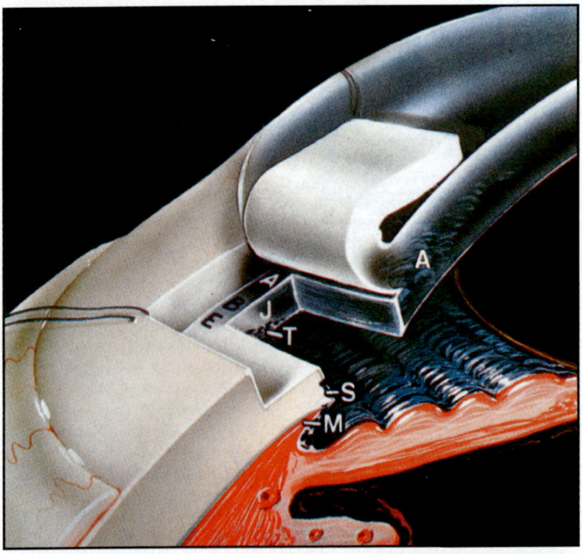

Figure 25: Modified "Tunnel" Trabeculectomy Technique - Final Configuration. This figure shows a cross section of the final trabeculectomy configuration. Note fornix-based scleral flap sclerocorneal bed (B), scleral flap (A), and trabeculectomy opening (T). (Art from Jaypee Highlights Medical Publishers, Inc.)

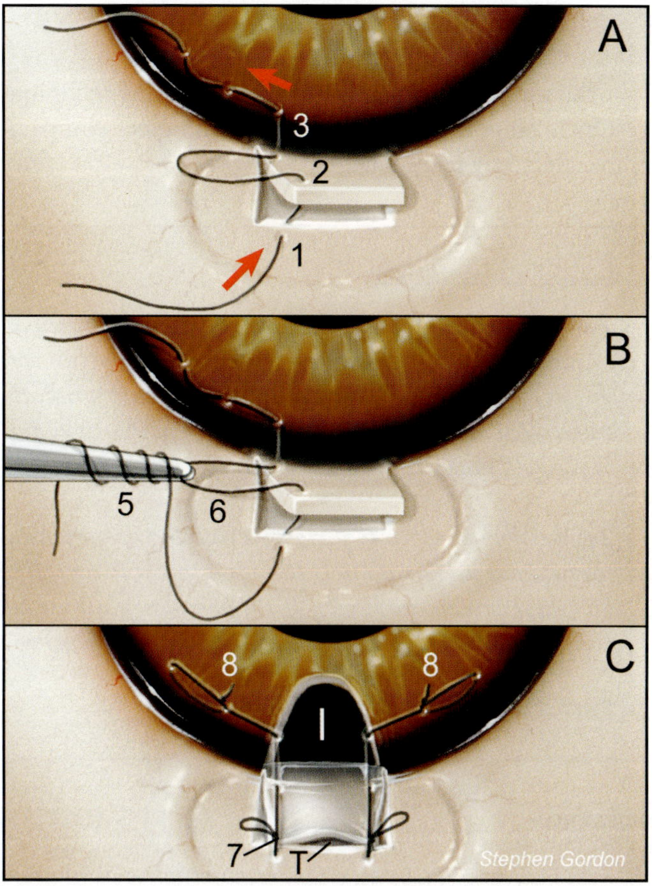

Figure 26 A-C: Modified "Tunnel" Trabeculectomy Technique - Suturing Technique. The lamellar scleral flap is sutured with two or more releasable 10-0 nylon interrupted sutures. (A) A scleral bite is taken in the posterior lip of the trabeculectomy scleral incision at the junction of the outer and middle third of the incision (1). Next, the needle is passed through the posterior corner of the lamellar scleral flap (2). Then a bite is taken at the base of the cornea into corneal tissue (3) and then another bite in the cornea (4), parallel to the limbus. (B) To tie, the posterior end of the suture is grasped with tying forceps and three throws made (5). The suture portion at the base of the cornea is grasped and pulled through the three loops (6), forming a bow-tie suture. (C) This knot is tightened onto the posterior lip of the scleral flap (7). When this configuration is tied tightly on both sides of the scleral flap, a central tunnel (T) is formed. The suture ends on the cornea are trimmed (8). The conjunctival flap is then sutured to the sclera at the limbus with a continuous 10-0 nylon suture (not shown). (Art from Jaypee Highlights Medical Publishers, Inc.)

Suturing the Lamellar Scleral Flap

The lamellar scleral flap is sutured with two releasable 10-0 nylon interrupted sutures, following the technique described by Allan Kolker, M.D. **(Figure 26)**.

Conclusion

The tunnel scleral incision trabeculectomy technique simplifies the operation, results in smoother surgical surfaces, and gives comparable results to the standard trabeculectomy technique.

Editorial Comment

The aim of glaucoma surgery is to reduce the intraocular pressure (IOP) in order to reduce the risk of progression of glaucomatous optic neuropathy, especially in cases that are refractory to treatment with medical therapy. Over the years, trabeculectomy has undergone variable modifications but is generally considered to be the gold standard for glaucoma surgery.

The decision on when to perform a filtering operation would depend on how close the field loss is to fixation. If there is a threat to central vision we should not wait and must proceed surgically. If the field loss is diffuse and mainly confined to the periphery, away from fixation, we can wait but observe the patient closely.

Samuel Boyd, MD. Editor-in-Chief.

References

1. Jay J. L., Allan D.: The Benefit of Early Trabeculectomy vs Conventional Management in Primary Open Angle Glaucoma, Eye 1989, 3: 528-535.
2. Sommer, A.: Improving our Understanding Between Pressure and Glaucoma, Highlights of Ophthalmol., Vol. XVIII Nº. 11, 1990, p. 1,7,8,10.
3. Hitchings, Roger: The Moorfields View on Primary Surgery for Open Angle Glaucoma, Guest Expert, Highlights of Ophthalmol. WORLD ATLAS SERIES, Vol. I, 1993.
4. Sommer, A.: AJO, 1989, 107: 186-8.
5. Pohjanpelto, P.E., Palva, J., Acta. Ophthal., 1974, 52:194-200.
6. Maurice H. Luntz, M.D., Abraham Schlossman, M.D. Trabeculectomy: A modified surgical technique, J. Cataract Refract. Surg. Vol. 20, Pages 350-352, 1994.
7. Cairns, J E: Trabeculectomy – Preliminary report of a new method. Am. J. Ophthalmol, 66 : 673- 679, 1968.
8. Wilson, RP and Lloyd, J: The Place of Sodium Hyaluronate in Glaucoma Surgery: Ophthalmic Surgery 17:30, 1986.
9. Boyd, B. F.: The Filtering Operations. World Atlas Series of Ophthalmic Surgery of Highlights of Ophthalmology,. Vol. I. 1993, pp.205-215.

3 The Use of Antimetabolites

Benjamin F. Boyd, MD, FACS
Maurice Luntz, MD, FACS

The two main drugs of real significance to enhance surgical success following trabeculectomy are: 1) 5-Fluorouracil (5-FU) which may be administered by subconjunctival injection during the immediate postoperative period or intraoperatively as a single application at the site of the scleral flap; and 2) Mitomycin which is administered with a single application applied with a sponge to the scleral bed of the already dissected trabeculectomy flap or over the area of full thickness sclera beneath the conjunctival flap, before dissection of the scleral flap or transconjunctivally before dissecting the conjunctival flap. Techniques vary with different surgeons, as well as the drug concentration used.

The advent and successful use of 5-FU and mitomycin are considered to be one of the most significant advances in glaucoma surgery, essentially because they are very useful anti-scarring medications in the treatment of glaucoma.

Excessive Scarring During Postoperative Period

Even if the operation is done perfectly, we have a group of variables of postoperative wound healing. We do not know why excessive scarring occurs in some patients **(Figures 1** and **2)**. On gonioscopic examination, most filtering sites show a patent internal sclerostomy after trabeculectomy **(Figure 2)**. Scarring begins at the episcleral surface and proceeds to seal down the trabeculectomy flap externally

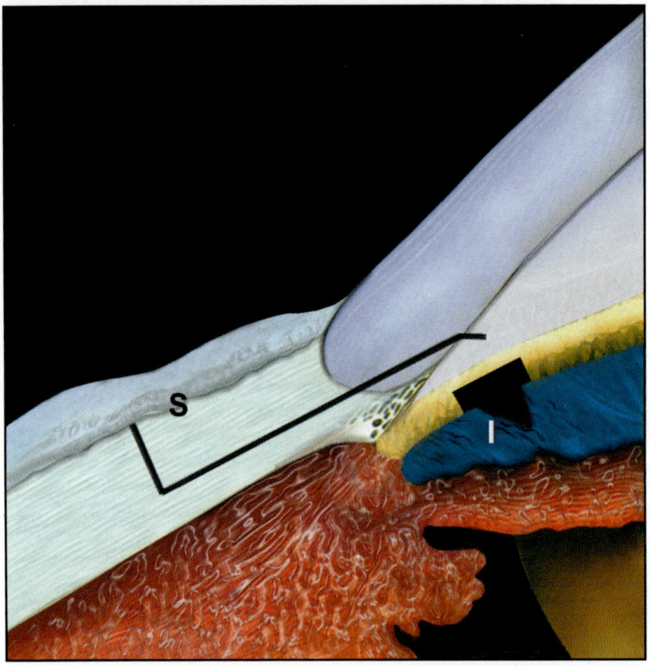

Figure 1: Excessive Scarring During Postoperative Wound Healing Leading to Poor Prognosis. The formation of scar tissue (S) is shown between episclera and conjunctiva. This closes the bleb causing failure of the filtration surgery. Iridectomy (I). Internal sclerostomy shown as a black square next to (I). (Art from Jaypee Highlights Medical Publishers, Inc.)

(Figure 1). Filtering operations do not heal from the inside out. The problem is not in maintaining an opening in the sclera, but with subsequent scarring at the episcleral/subconjunctival interface. Thus, external scarring seems to give some patients a poor prognosis after surgery. It is in this group of patients that the antimetabolites are specifically recommended.

Preoperative Conditions Contributing to Failure

Patients for whom filtration surgery is likely to fail and who therefore are specific candidates for the use of antimetabolites, can generally be divided into four groups with the following preoperative variables as outlined by Parrish[1]: The first group, which is becoming increasingly large, includes patients with aphakic or pseudo-phakic eyes. It is not known why aphakic or pseudophakic eyes make it more difficult to achieve successful filtration, but clearly they do. A second important variable is relative youth. For patients less than 50 years of age who are

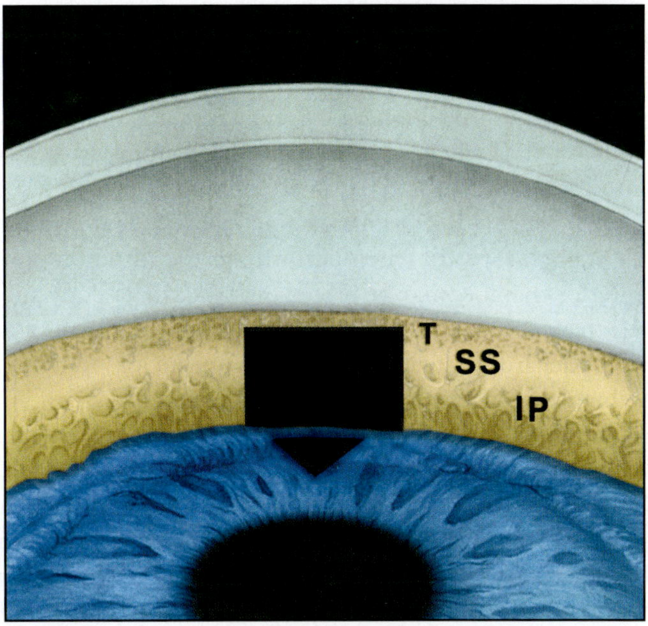

Figure 2: Postoperative Gonioscopic View Showing Patent Internal Sclerostomy After Trabeculectomy. A gonioscopic view allows visualization of the trabecular meshwork (T), scleral spur (SS), and iris processes (IP) as well as the patent internal sclerostomy and iridectomy. Filtering operations do not heal from the inside out. (Art from Jaypee Highlights Medical Publishers, Inc.)

also aphakic or pseudophakic, the success rate is only one in twenty, according to the studies of Gressel, Heuer and Parrish[2]. The third group includes patients who have had unsuccessful filtration surgery in the past. If a first filtration procedure has failed, we know the likelihood that a second filtration operation will fail is higher than usual. The fourth group includes patients with neovascular glaucoma, irrespective of the etiology of the neovascularization (diabetic or central retinal vein occlusion).

Another major preoperative cause of failure is the race of the patient. Black patients tend to scar more actively and aggressively than Caucasians, and they have a higher failure rate. Another cause of failure is scarring of the conjunctiva from previous surgery, particularly previous filter surgery. In all these situations, the use of antimetabolites has greatly improved the success rate.

Intraoperative Variables Contributing to Failure

In addition to the preoperative variables that determine a higher likelihood of failure in the four high-risk groups just described, there are intraoperative variables, such as when an inadequate sclerectomy is created, or the iris incarcerates into the wound, or vitreous is present in the filtration surgery site.

In cases with previous cataract surgery, if we do not dissect the conjunctiva far enough forward when performing the filtration operation, the entry into the anterior chamber may be placed over the ciliary body and cause excessive bleeding. All these events are more likely to occur in the high-risk groups.

Richard Parrish, M.D. and a group of ophthalmologists at the Bascom Palmer Eye Institute in Florida pioneered the use of antimetabolites, specifically 5-fluorouracil (5-FU) and mitomycin C (MMC) in filtering surgery. Even today, surgeons tend to use antimetabolites more conservatively in appreciation of the late-onset complications, such as thin walled blebs that may predispose to the development of bleb leaks, endophthalmitis, and hypotony maculopathy.

Surgeons tend to use a slightly lower concentration of mitomycin C for a shorter duration than initially described. The concentration of mitomycin C used most frequently is 0.4 mg/ml for 3 to 4 minutes rather than 0.5 mg/ml for 5 minutes, as originally suggested by Dr. David Palmer, who introduced the use of mitomycin C to American ophthalmologists.

Many variables in the application of antimetabolites cannot be determined simply by assessing the concentration and the length of exposure. How the antimetabolite is applied and later removed may influence the drug concentration and the ultimate clinical outcome.

Use of 5-Fluorouracil

During many years, surgeons have moved toward the use of intraoperative 5-FU in a manner similar to that used for mitomycin C. (*Editor's Note*: Many surgeons use 5-FU in patients with low to moderate risk and Mitomycin in high risk eyes.) Commercially 5-FU (Adrucil) is available at a concentration 50 mg/ml. Undiluted 5-FU is usually applied on a cellulose cell or sponge fragment to the episcleral surface over the area of the planned trabeculectomy directly beneath and in contact with the conjunctival flap. Some surgeons outline the trabeculectomy flap and then apply the sponge to the scleral surface. If the sponge soaked with either mitomycin C or 5-FU is placed on the sclera and the conjunctiva is pulled superiorly and posteriorly against the globe, additional fluid with the antimetabolite is squeezed from the sponge. Parrish prefers to dry the episcleral surface with a dry cellulose sponge to quickly absorb as much of the antimetabolite from the surgical field after application, prior to irrigation with 10 ml sterile saline solution. Other surgeons simply irrigate the area copiously.

Use of Mitomycin C

The use of intraoperative mitomycin C in eyes with good prognosis is decreasing. Patients less than 50 years old and African Americans are more likely to be treated with intraoperative mitomycin C than 5-FU. A key to surgical success to prevent immediate postoperative hypotony with mitomycin C is to ensure that the flap is tightly sutured. Placing sufficiently tight sutures that can be either cut with an argon laser or released sequentially helps minimize immediate postoperative hypotony. If only two sutures are placed in the scleral flap and the intraocular pressure remains elevated after cutting or releasing the first suture, the risk of hypotony is substantial when the only remaining suture is cut. Placing three or four 10-0 nylon sutures and cutting them sequentially minimizes the risk of this development. The effects of mitomycin C on delaying wound healing are prolonged and sutures may be cut or released up to one month after trabeculectomy and still result in profound intraocular pressure lowering.

Indications for Antimetabolites

The main and specific indications for the use of antimetabolites are: 5-FU in the low to moderate and intermediate risk patients and mitomycin in the high risk groups, because of its toxicity. An increasing number of surgeons, however, are using mitomycin routinely in lower concentrations. 5-FU is being used more regularly by subconjunctival injection postoperatively in routine cases that present early signs of possible bleb failure. 5-FU can be used in a single application intraoperatively and is somewhat less toxic than mitomycin, but not as effective.

THE USE OF 5-FU

Subconjunctival Administration Postoperatively

5-FU is usually given postoperatively at the first sign of vascular ingrowth into the bleb, thickening of the bleb or increasing intraocular pressure in the early postoperative period. Characteristically on the second or third postoperative day, after allowing the wound to heal 2 or 3 days following surgery. Delayed administration of 5-FU has allowed him to avoid most wound leaks. If the delay is only 2 or 3 days, scarring of the bleb does not usually have time to occur.

At the first signs of vascular ingrowth and thickening of the bleb, you should inject it daily, hopefully until the scarring reverses or the patient can not tolerate further administration.

The dosage for each injection is 5 mg (0.1 cc or ml). The vial usually contains 10cc. The cost is about US$8.00 per vial. It is very important to inject 5-FU at the slit lamp. Proparacaine anesthesia and a drop of phenylephrine will vasoconstrict the vessels and decrease the incidence of bleeding, which can otherwise be a problem. The injection is given subconjunctivally into the fornix in the periphery of the bulbar conjunctiva. Injecting too close to the bleb can create a leak merely from the passage of the needle into the filtering tissues. These injections are continued daily until toxicity develops or until the fibrosis of the bleb ceases and a good functional bleb is established.

Tolerability of 5-FU

Tolerability is an important limitation of 5-FU. Some extremely sensitive patients develop irritation and discomfort after the first two or three injections, and others tolerate 20 or 25 injections before they show any signs of toxicity. On the average, a patient will exhibit toxicity after seven or eight injections of 5-FU. The important toxicity occurs in the epithelium of the cornea. 5-FU seems to inhibit the proliferation of stem cells that regenerate the epithelium of the cornea in the limbal region. In patients who manifest this effect, the epithelium becomes thin, then stippled and often totally absent. Upon cessation of 5-FU administration the epithelial cells will begin to grow again, usually after 14 to 20 days. Subsequent to the last injection the epithelium will regenerate essentially in all cases. Absence of the epithelium yields an unpleasant foreign body sensation and also causes reflex congestion of the conjunctiva.

Stamper points out that any time that you have something that makes your therapy more effective, you cannot expect to get away without some problems.[3] And 5-Fluorouracil is no exception. The problems that are most frequently encountered with 5-Fluorouracil are related to the very things that we want 5-Fluorouracil to do. We want it to prevent or slow down the scarring-healing. Unfortunately, 5-Fluorouracil does not discriminate. So it does not discriminate between a fibroblast, which is our enemy, and a conjunctival or corneal epithelial cell which is our friend. With 5-Fluorouracil, the division of the new corneal epithelial cells is going to be inhibited. So, you get wound leaks and corneal toxicity that ranges anywhere from punctate keratopathy to frank corneal abrasions. Those are the most common.

Use of Bandage Contact Lens to Increase Tolerability

A large bandage contact lens will minimize 5-FU's side effects and greatly improve the patient's tolerance of 5-FU administration. The bandage contact lens, which covers the cornea, reduces the foreign body sensation and the reflex congestion of the eye due to the epithelial defect . It therefore allows prolonged administration of 5-FU, usually until the patient no longer needs it and bleb scarring has ceased.

A bleb leak following 5-FU injections is treated with a large bandage contact lens (22 mm diameter) which extends into the periphery of the fornix covering the wound itself . This allows the conjunctival wound to be supported and a good filtration bleb that retains fluid to be developed. Eventually, when the 5-FU injections cease, the cornea has cleared, the epithelium has regenerated, and the wound has healed, he removes the bandage contact lens.

On the other hand, if in spite of these therapeutic measures the patient is in pain, the cornea is getting hazier, or the wound is breaking down, you quit. But if none of these occurs and the scarring process is decreasing, the bleb is getting better and the eye is quiet, you might continue 5-FU administration until your clinical judgment leads you to stop.

Most surgeons limit 5-FU to 10 injections of 5mg each, a total of 50mg. If the cornea remains unaffected, a higher dose of 5-FU can be given.

Wound Leaks

Another side effect is that in some patients the wound, which originally was sealed and appeared healed, begins to leak at approximately 5-10 days after initiation of 5-FU therapy. This can occur with limbal based or fornix based conjunctival flaps, but is more common in the latter.

Meticulous closure of the conjunctiva is very helpful to prevent conjunctival wound leaks. Stamper[3] recommended an atraumatic needle **(Figure 3)** and tries to make the incision in the conjunctiva fairly far from the limbus so that the aqueous drainage is as far away from the conjunctival incision as possible. He closes the conjunctiva with a running 11-0 Mersilene suture on an atraumatic, non-cutting needle, so that the needle does not cut any bigger hole in the conjunctiva than absolutely necessary **(Figure 3)**. It is impressive sometimes to see leaks coming out of the suture tracks, even when you use such fine sutures as 10-0 and 11-0. We really have to handle conjunctiva more delicately than we have in the past.

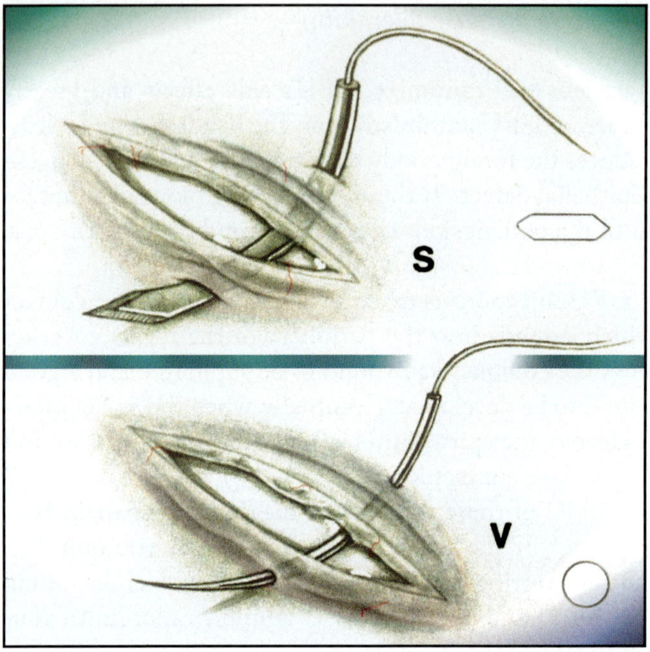

Figure 3: Minimizing Wound Leaks When Using Antimetabolites. Tight wound closure is essential for conjunctival healing. The top diagram illustrates how the spatula needle (S) creates a wide slit in the conjunctiva which allows wound leakage because the suture does not fill the hole created by the needle. A cross section of the needle is shown adjacent to the view of the entire needle. The lower diagram shows how a vascular-taper needle (V) minimizes wound leakage. The diameter of the needle and the diameter of the suture are nearly the same which allows for tight wound closure. This needle is round in cross section. (Art from Jaypee Highlights Medical Publishers, Inc.)

Results With 5-FU

With the method and precautions described, in those cases of eyes that have not had previous surgery one expects 75 to 80% success rate without 5-FU but with 5-Fluorouracil the success rate is into the 90% range.

Luntz has observed that the effect of antimetabolites used with filtration surgery lead to an additional drop in the intraocular pressure of approximately 20%. The main benefit from antimetabolites, however, is that they significantly increase the number of blebs that filter.

Rationale for Using 5-FU

The rationale for using 5-FU is that it interferes with the synthesis of both DNA and RNA. In rapidly growing fibroblasts, as in rapidly growing tumor cells, if the replication of DNA can be stopped, we can halt or substantially diminish the proliferation of the cell. Since the fibroblast is the primary culprit in filtering-surgery failure **(Figure 1)**, slowing its growth increases the success of filtration surgery.

We know that the area, degree and length of fibroblast inhibition can be controlled by varying the concentration or type of agent, and potentially this may enable us to control bleb position, thickness and possibly even titrate the final intraocular pressure. [4]

When to Use 5-FU and When Mitomycin

5-FU is indicated in a single application as previously described or by subconjunctival injection postoperatively in patients with low or moderate risk factors, including patients under 40, Afro-Caribbeans and those who have been using topical medications for more than one year, especially pilocarpine or adrenaline. It may also be considered useful in patients with intermediate risk factors such as previous conjunctival surgery including trabeculectomy and cataract surgery. When used as described, it has lowered failure rate to less than half the former levels.

Mitomycin, on the other hand, is a more potent and toxic drug, leading to avascular and cystic blebs which may result in a high incidence of leaks and endophthalmitis in the future. It is indicated in eyes which have failed with a previous trabeculectomy with 5-FU, glaucoma with uveitis, glaucoma with chronic conjunctival inflammation, aphakia and multiple risk factors.

The use of mitomycin and 5-FU in filtering glaucoma surgery is very important since it has been demonstrated that the lower the final intraocular pressure after surgery the better the visual prognosis. The main reason for surgical failure and suboptimal lowering of intraocular pressure is the scarring response after glaucoma filtration surgery. The use of the antimetabolites has considerably reduced the failure rate and also results in a lower final intraocular pressure.

THE USE OF MITOMYCIN

There is some controversy about how mitomycin acts. Although some investigators feel that it is cidal to the fibroblast, there is some tissue culture work which suggests that, while the fibroblasts are inhibited from replicating for four to six weeks, they are still viable after the application of mitomycin. Simmons considers that this work is very significant because it suggests that mitomycin is just what we want in terms of a fibroblast inhibitor. It also explains the very promising results obtained up to this point. An important concern is the long term effect of this drug on these blebs. Some of them become quite thin and avascular causing concern about the potential long-term risk of breakdown and infection leading to endophthalmitis.

Method of Application of Mitomycin

Some surgeons are using mitomycin routinely but in lower concentrations. A solution of 0.2 mg/ml mitomycin is prepared by mixing the contents of a 5-mg vial of mitomycin into 25 ml of sterile water; a Weck cell sponge is soaked in the mitomycin and applied directly to the scleral flap for approximately 4 minutes.[7]

Arenas has modified his trabeculectomy ab-externo to facilitate the opening of the external wall of Schlemm's canal and allow him to use mitomycin routinely in trabeculectomy ab-externo applying a sponge with very diluted doses of the drug (0.04 mg per ml, one tenth the standard dose of 0.4 mg per ml).

Arenas uses this technique with simple application of very diluted doses of mitomycin in all his cases, provided he does not enter the anterior chamber. There is no risk of damaging the corneal endothelium or any other structure of the eye if the anterior chamber is not entered. It is important, however, that he does use a much weaker dose of mitomycin as outlined above. Arenas[16] has used mitomycin routinely in many cases of trabeculectomy ab-externo and fortunately have had no flat chambers or other complications.

Some surgeons put the mitomycin underneath the scleral flap **(Figure 4).**

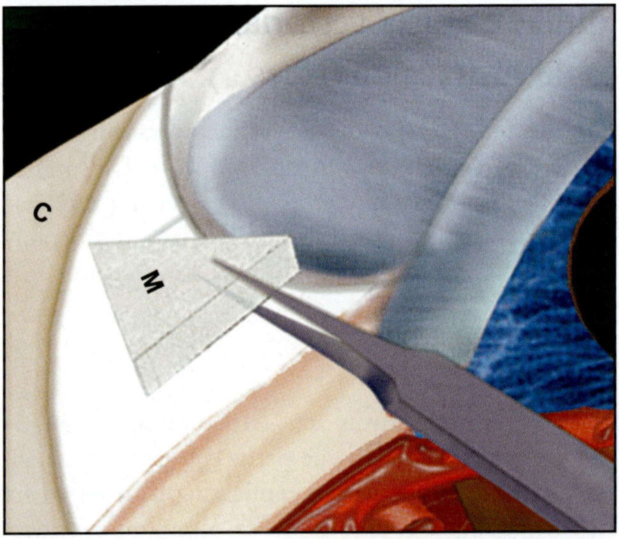

Figure 4: Mitomycin Soaked Sponge Placed Directly over Sclera. The cellulose sponge soaked with a 0.4 mg per cc dilution of mitomycin (M) is placed during four minutes directly on top of the sclera in the area where the scleral flap will be dissected. Some surgeons prefer to apply the mitomycin over the scleral bed of the trabeculectomy, underneath the scleral flap but these constitute a minority. Do not enter the eye prior to the application of the mitomycin. Fornix based conjunctival flap (C). (Art from Jaypee Highlights Medical Publishers, Inc.)

Some surgeons apply the mitomycin on the episclera before dissecting the outer trabeculectomy scleral flap. Others prefer to dissect the scleral flap and apply the sponge on the scleral bed of the trabeculectomy flap. It is most important not to enter the eye prior to the application of mitomycin because this drug is very powerful and if a leak occurs it can cause extensive intraocular damage.

It is important not to expose the cut back edge of the conjunctival flap to the sponge. This helps conjunctival wound closure without leaks.

Mitomycin blebs seem to fall into two groups. The first group looks rather like a 5-Fluorouracil filter with a very diffuse pale and thin but not avascular bleb. These occur about half the time. The other half of the blebs are thin, clear, white and sharply demarcated. Why the bleb tissue does not become re-vascularized or scars as it would if killed by some other agents such as cautery or alcohol, nobody knows for certain.

Luntz[5] titrates the dosage of mitomycin applied at the time of filtration surgery to minimize the risk of complications. The titration is achieved as follows:

1) A standard 0.4% solution is used.

2) If the lowest titration is required, the mitomycin is applied to the conjunctiva via a soaked cell sponge for 3-4 minutes, depending on the dosage the surgeon selects. Then the sponge is carefully removed, and the area of the surgery treated with mitomycin is profusely irrigated with balanced salt or saline solution.

3) If a higher dose is required, four minutes of mitomycin are applied to the conjunctiva, and, following a peritomy, mitomycin is applied under the conjunctiva for 1-3 minutes. Again the area of the surgery treated with mitomycin is profusely irrigated with balanced salt or saline solution **(Figure 5)**.

The dosage applied will depend on the degree of scarring in the conjunctiva and whether the patient is caucasian or pigmented. In lightly scarred conjunctivae in the caucasian patient, the transconjunctival application is used for 3-4 minutes. In more heavily scarred conjunctiva from previous surgery in a caucasian patient, one would use four minutes applied to the conjunctiva and 1-2 minutes applied under the conjunctiva. In pigmented patients or caucasian patients under 40 years of age, in uveitis, for the initial surgery, one would use four minutes of mitomycin applied to the conjunctiva. In pigmented patients who have had previous surgery with moderate scarring, one would use four minutes of application on the conjunctiva and 1-2 minutes under the conjunctiva. In pigmented patients with previous surgery and a heavily scarred conjunctiva, one would use the full dosage of four minutes applied on the conjunctiva and three minutes applied under the conjunctiva. Each surgeon needs to apply his/her own judgment in terms of dosage to each individual case.

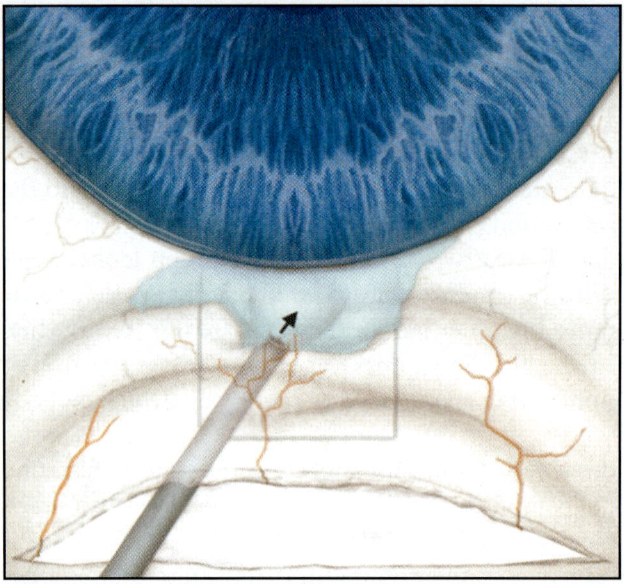

Figure 5: Profuse Irrigation After Removal of Mitomycin Sponge. After the cellulose sponge is removed, the area of the surgery treated with mitomycin is profusely irrigated with balanced salt or saline solution. It is very important that all the antimetabolite be irrigated from the field. When using mitomycin, a larger amount of irrigating fluid is used than when using a single application of 5-FU. Mitomycin is much more toxic. (Art from Jaypee Highlights Medical Publishers, Inc.)

Transconjunctival Application

A 0.4% solution of mitomycin is drawn into a tuberculin syringe up to the 2cc mark. The syringe is emptied into a glass dish. Three or four cell sponges are cut across the tip of the sponge (leaving a rectangular-shaped sponge). These sponges are then soaked in the mitomycin in the Petrie dish. The patient's conjunctiva is evaluated and the site for the surgery selected. One cell sponge is then applied to the site for one minute, discarded, and the second cell sponge applied for one minute, etc., for 3-4 minutes, depending on the dosage that the surgeon has selected for that patient. Up to four minutes of transconjunctival application can be used.

Subconjunctival Application

In this case, the surgeon has decided on a higher dosage than four minutes of transconjunctival application. Following four minutes of transconjunctival application, the mitomycin is thoroughly washed from the conjunctival surface with balanced salt solution. A peritomy is performed at the site of the surgery, forming a fornix-based flap which is then dissected from the sclera to form a subconjunctival pocket. Taking a cell sponge, four small pieces of sponge are cut and soaked in the mitomycin solution. Each of these four small sponges soaked with mitomycin is placed under the conjunctiva for one minute. Depending on the dosage that the surgeon has selected, two, three or four of these sponges are used, giving a dose of two, three or four minutes of exposure to the mitomycin. Following this procedure, the mitomycin is thoroughly washed from the subconjunctival space with balanced salt solution **(Figure 5).** The surgeon selects a minimal dose of mitomycin that he/she considers adequate for each individual case, and, in this way, attempts to minimize the postoperative complications from mitomycin.

Editorial Comment

The rapid acceptance of the adjunctive use of antimetabolites in conjunction with filtering glaucoma surgery may be at least partially a consequence of changing medical-social-economic factors, rather than solely a desire on the part of physicians to improve the success of glaucoma surgery. This may indicate a need to reevaluate the proper place of antimetabolites in association with filtration surgery.

Samuel Boyd, MD. Editor-in-Chief.

References

1. Parrish R : Personal communication
2. Gressel M G, Heuer D K, Parrish R K : Trabeculectomy in Young Patients, Ophthalmology 1984, 91 : 1242 – 1246.
3. Stamper, R : Highlights of Ophthalmology, World Atlas Series, Vol. I, 1992, Page 278.
4. Khaw P T et al : Highlights of Ophthalmology, World Atlas Series, Vol. I, 1992, Page 276.
5. Luntz, M H and Harrison R : Glaucoma Surgery, 2nd Edition, Series Ed, A S M Lim, PG Publishing, World Scientific, Singapore, 1994, Page 108.
6. Arenas, M : Personal communication.
7. Boyd, B.F.: The Use of Antimetabolites in Glaucoma Surgery, World Atlas Series of Ophthalmic Surgery of Highlights of Ophthalmology. Vol I, 1993, pp. 226 - 232.
8. Palmberg, P.: Prevention and Management of Complicated Hypotony in Trabeculectomy with Mitomycin, in Boyd, B.F.'s, Highlights of Ophthalmology Journal. Vol. 21, 1993, Series 9, pp. 67-77.

4 The Arenas' Ab Externo Trabeculectomy Technique

Eduardo Arenas A., MD, FACS

The Ab-Externo technique is based on a physiological concept: it removes the diseased endothelial layer of Schlemm's canal (which is the site of highest resistance to outflow present in open angle glaucoma) resulting in normal flow of aqueous humor outside the eye.[1,2] It can be employed by two different maneuvers: One using a micro diamond drill in order to unroof SC and avoid the risk of accidental perforation of the anterior chamber which is one of the most frequent complications of non-penetrating filtering operations[3], particularly during the learning curve **(Figure 1)**. Schlemm's canal (SC) is first unroofed by dissection of a deep scleral flap or with the microdrill **(Figure 1)**. Second we have devised a simple tool named hook maker, where with the aid of a 30 gauge needle assembled in a handle it is possible to create a micro hook, making it possible to remove microscopically slowly the tissue and fibers of the floor of the SC, until a permanent flow of aqueous is reached, keeping the anterior chamber completely formed **(Figures 2A and 2 B)**.

With the drill the surgeon achieves a micro communication of the floor (inner wall) of Schlemm's canal to the anterior chamber **(Figure 1)**. The aqueous humor in Schlemm's canal begins to pour out. Then the surgeon drills out the microscopic layer of diseased endothelium **(Figure 1-E)** that makes up the floor of Schlemm's canal, which constitutes the site of greatest resistance to outflow. What remain

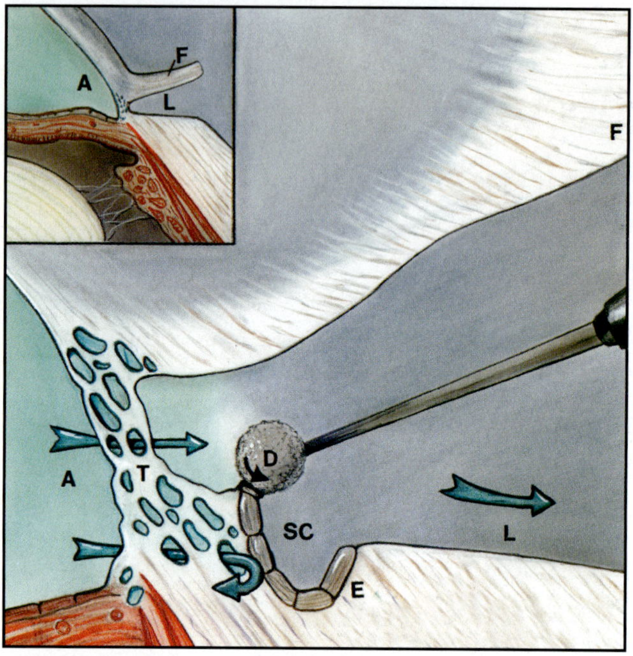

Figure 1: Arenas' Ab-Externo Technique. Schlemm's canal is first unroofed by dissection or with a micro diamond drill. The surgeon then uses the diamond drill (D) to remove the diseased endothelium (E) of the floor of Schlemm's canal (SC). What remains are several layers of very thin trabecular fibers (T) between the opened Schlemm's canal and the anterior chamber (A). These layers of trabecular meshwork protect the anterior chamber and prevent herniation of the iris. After the ab-externo procedure the trabecular meshwork is the only structure separating the anterior chamber (A) from the conjunctiva. This facilitates improved filtration through the trabecular meshwork into the subconjunctival tissues and leading to the formation of a filtering subconjunctival bleb. (L) indicates the space created by lifting and eventual removal of the scleral flap (F). (Art from Jaypee Highlights Medical Publishers, Inc.)

are several layers of very thin, trabecular fibers between the opened Schlemm's canal and the anterior chamber. The presence of these layers of trabecular meshwork at this site protect the integrity of the anterior chamber (no loss in depth) and prevent herniation of the iris. The trabecular meshwork remains as the only structure separating the anterior chamber from the conjunctiva after the Ab Externo procedure. The aqueous filters through the remaining trabecular meshwork toward a subconjunctival bleb. (*Editor's Note*: for step by step technique, see **Figures 2 - 8.**)

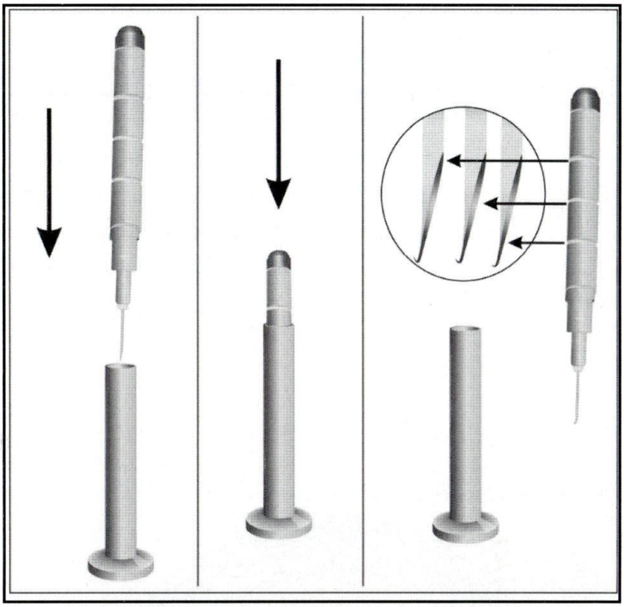

Figure 2A: Hook Maker device. At the left side of the figure a 26 gauge ½ inch hypodermic needle has been attached to a steel special handle and will be dropped to a cylinder container at different distances depending on the angle of the hook desired by the surgeon. In the middle of the drawing the handle has been dropped into the cylinder vertically. At the right side is shown the different curvatures of the hook. The lower the handle is dropped the finer the dissection tool achieved.

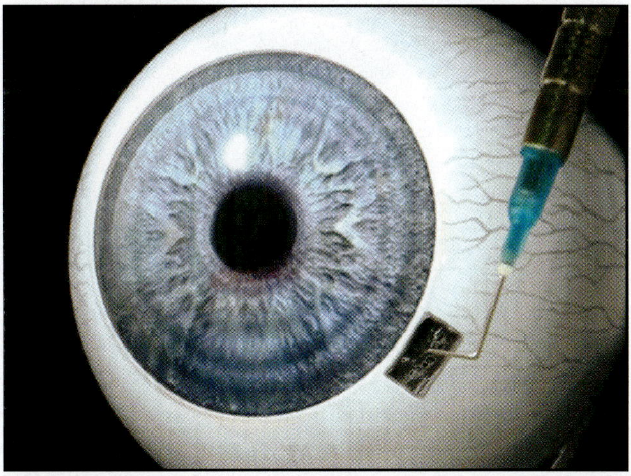

Figure 2B: Drawing showing the Schlemm´s canal unroofed ready to be slowly dissected with the hook maker.

Main Advantages

The significant advantages of this procedure are the following:

1.) The ab-externo trabeculectomy is a noninvasive fistulizing procedure which allows spontaneous, continuous filtration of aqueous after removal of the external walls of Schlemm's canal **(Figures 2, 3, 4, 5)**.[4,5] The internal wall of the canal is slightly severed with a diamond drill especially designed by Arenas for this operation (Figure 7).

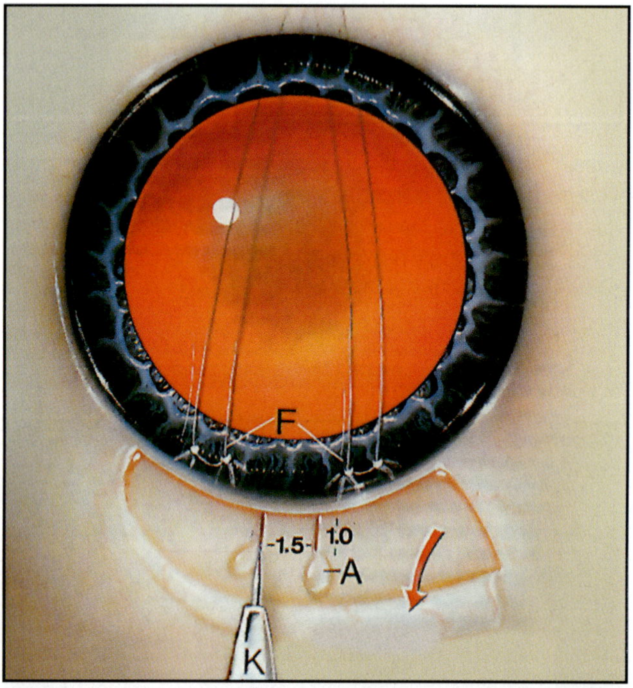

Figure 3A: Ab-externo Trabeculectomy - Stage 1 – Initial Steps and Ab-externo Incision. The procedure begins with two 7-0 silk fixation sutures placed deeply in the cornea (F). A fornix based "L" shaped conjunctival flap is reflected (arrow) with the aid of Weck cell microsponges that avoid bleeding. In this moment intrascleral lydocaine is injected at the site of the sclera incision. Two parallel incisions are made 1.5 mm apart, starting at the limbus and extending posteriorly for 1 mm. Cautery is applied at the borders of the incisions to permit a shrinking of the borders and in an ab-externo fashion the flap is deepened at one end, until a small leakage of aqueous (A) is obtained. This leakage shows that the external wall of Schlemm's canal has been reached. (Art from Jaypee Highlights Medical Publishers, Inc.)

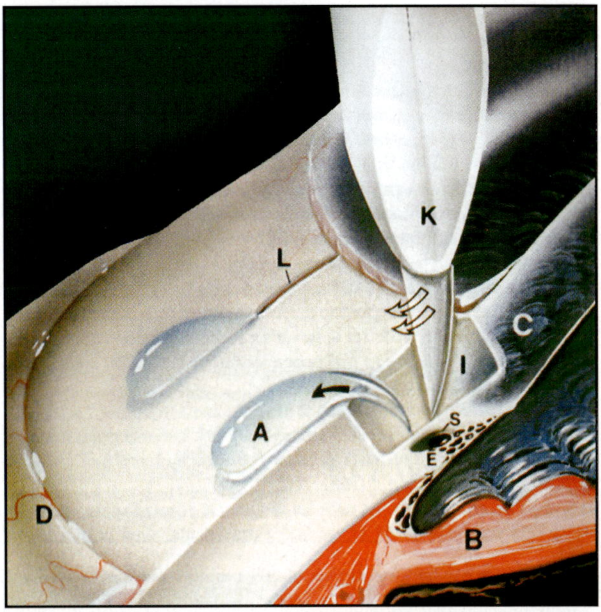

Figure 3B: Ab-externo Trabeculectomy - Stage 1 – Initial Steps and Ab-externo Incision - Cross Section. The above oblique cross section view shows the 1 mm ab-externo incision (I) being made with a razor knife (K). The knife makes passes of ever-increasing depth (white arrows) until a small leakage of aqueous (A - black arrow) is obtained. Notice that the knife has nearly reached a depth of Schlemm's canal (S). The completed left ab-externo incision (L) also presents aqueous. Other anatomy: Iris (B), cornea (C), reflected conjunctiva (D), scleral spur (E). (Art from Jaypee Highlights Medical Publishers, Inc.)

2.) Because it is an extraocular procedure, retrobulbar or peribulbar block is not necessary.[6] Local anesthesia is used at the beginning of the surgery with Tetracaine facilitating a dissection of a fornix based flap and only before starting the sclera flap a small quantity of lidocaine is injected in the episclera at the site of the rectangular flap. No flat chambers occur postoperatively because the anterior chamber is not entered for the fistulizing procedure. This is a microscopic filtering operation.[7,8]

3.) Mitomycin can be used in all cases because the drug's concentration is a good deal less (0.08 mg/cc instead of the usual 0.2 mg to 0.4 mg/cc). Arenas has found this dosage to be sufficient and effective. Because of the low concentration it can be applied to the bed of the scleral flap but with a sponge large enough that will reach and exert its effect on the overlying conjunctiva without touching the edges of the conjuntival flap. Otherwise, healing of the flap would be affected **(Figure 6)**.

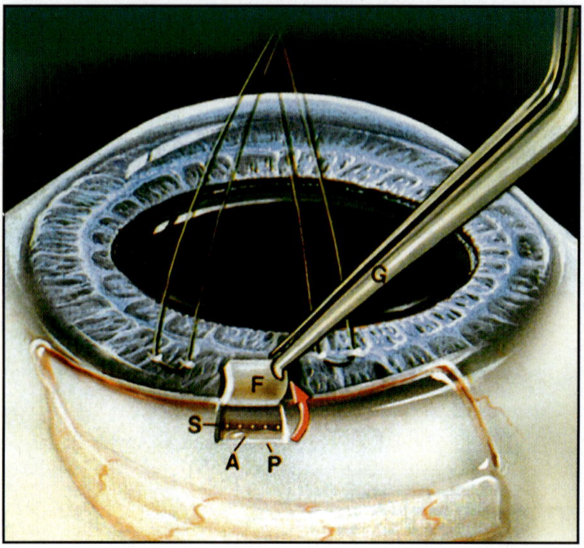

Figure 4: Ab-externo Trabeculectomy - Stage 2 - Creation of Microflap. At the moment when aqueous is obtained, the two parallel incisions are joined with an incision (P) at their posterior aspects. A small rectangular scleral flap (F) is formed and reflected (arrow) with a forceps (G). Usually a flow of aqueous (A) is observed at the base of the rectangular scleral bed. The origin of this aqueous is Schlemm's canal (S - dot shaded area) which can be observed on the scleral bed. (Art from Jaypee Highlights Medical Publishers, Inc.)

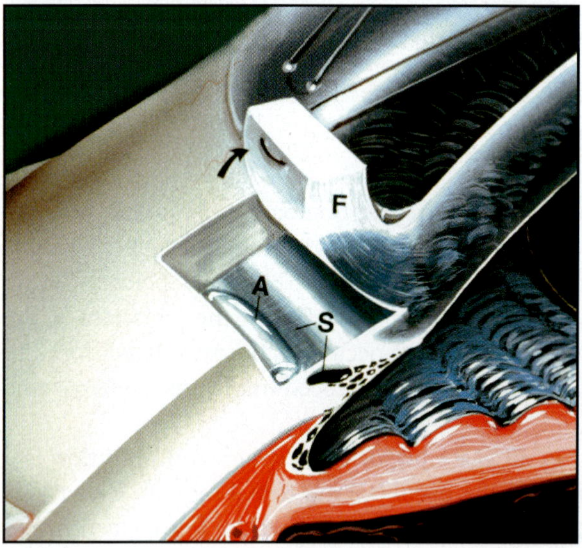

Figure 5: Ab-externo Trabeculectomy - Stage 2 - Creation of Microflap. This oblique cross section view shows the scleral flap (F) being reflected (arrow) with forceps (G), revealing Schlemm's canal (S) on the resulting scleral bed. Note the aqueous (A) at the bottom of the rectangular scleral bed. (Art from Jaypee Highlights Medical Publishers, Inc.)

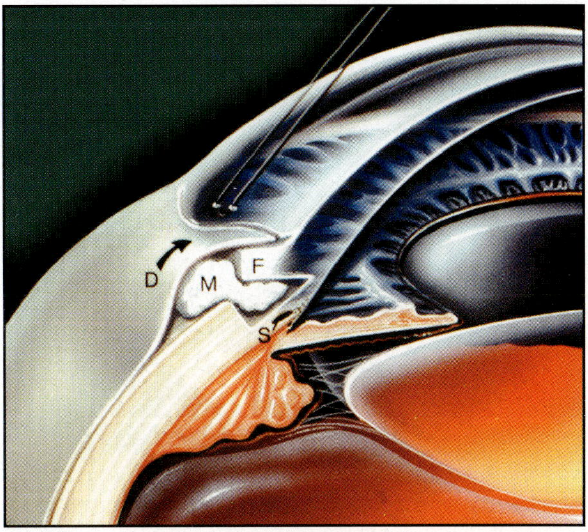

Figure 6: Ab-externo Trabeculectomy - Stage 3 – Application of Mitomycin. This oblique cross section shows the Weck sponge soaked with a 0.08 concentration of Mitomycin (M) placed over Schlemm's canal (S) and under the micro-scleral flap (F). The sponge must also reach the overlying conjunctiva and exert the effect of mitomycin on the conjunctiva and the bed of the scleral flap. The conjunctiva (D) covers (arrows) this area. The mitomycin sponge is left in place for three minutes. (Art from Jaypee Highlights Medical Publishers, Inc.)

4.) The microscopic filtration is obtained by means of a highly sophisticated diamond drill which spins at 8000 revolutions per minute in the bed of the scleral flap until reaching and slightly severing the internal wall of Schlemm's canal **(Figure 7)**.

5.) This procedure can be easily adapted to using it as a combined operation with extracapsular extraction or with phacoemulsification.

6.) At the end of the operation, the surgeon should check the amount of aqueous exiting the eye. It should be microscopic but continuous. If insufficient, additional but slight drilling of the internal wall of Schlemm's canal can be made at that time before closure of the conjunctiva.

Arenas advocates that with this technique continuous leaking of aqueous is produced that avoids the proliferation of fibrous tissue and promptly guarantees the formation of a bleb that will result in lowering of intraocular pressure.

Figure 7: Ab-externo Trabeculectomy - Stage 4 - Drilling of Schlemm's Canal. The conjunctiva (D) and microflap (F) are reflected and Mitomycin sponge removed. Arenas' diamond drill (H) spinning at 8000 revolutions per minute, is used to slowly deepen the area over Schlemm's canal (S) until the internal wall of the canal is severed. This will produce a more intense and permanent outflow of aqueous (arrows). This microscopic filtering procedure has completely preserved the anterior chamber. (Art from Jaypee Highlights Medical Publishers, Inc.)

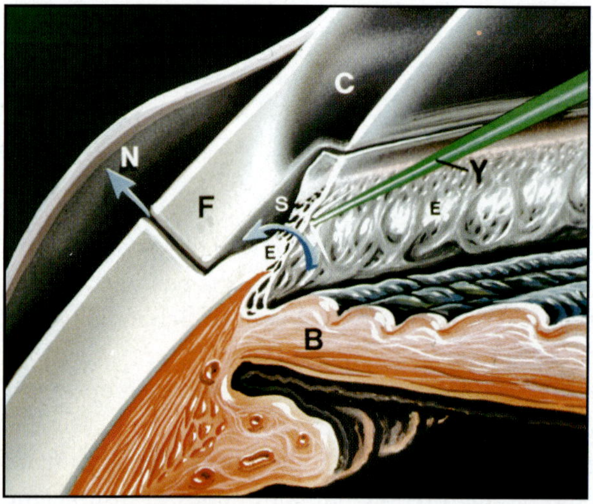

Figure 8: YAG Laser Trabeculolysis Postoperatively. If the intraocular pressure tends to be higher than 10 in the first postoperative days, a YAG trabeculolysis is performed. This gonioscopic cross section shows the YAG laser beam (Y) effecting a burn over the area of opened Schlemm's canal (S), under the microflap (F) of the filtering zone. This burn will create an improved passageway for aqueous flow (arrows) under the microflap and into the filtering bleb (N). Other anatomy: Scleral spur (E) seen gonioscopically and in cross section, cornea (C), and iris (B). (Art from Jaypee Highlights Medical Publishers, Inc.)

Immediate and Short Term Evolution - Post-Op Management

Close monitoring of the intraocular pressure is important. Within the first 24 hours, the intraocular pressure is around 5 mm Hg. It slowly reaches 10 to 15 mm Hg by the end of the third week without any anti-glaucoma medication.

If the intraocular pressure reaches levels higher than 10 mm Hg by the first week post-op, Arenas performs a YAG laser trabeculolysis through a Goldmann gonioscopic lens to improve the passage way for aqueous flow under the microflap **(Figure 8)**. Usually two shots with an intensity of 6 to 7 millijoules focused at the filtering zone in the angle are sufficient to lower again the pressure at desirable levels.

Editorial Comment

Criteria for surgical success in the treatment of congenital glaucoma mostly comprise resolution of the corneal oedema, stabilization of the horizontal corneal diameters, axial length, and the cup-disc ratio, while tolerable intraocular pressure varies from 14 up to 22 mm Hg. Prognosis of any surgery in primary congenital glaucoma is strongly influenced by the individual risk factors.

Samuel Boyd, MD. Editor-in-Chief.

Biblliography

1. Luntz MH, Livingstone DG.Trabeculotomy ab externo and trabeculectomy in congenital and adult onset glaucoma. Am J Ophthalmol 1977;83:174–9.
2. Quigley HA. Childhood glaucoma: Results with trabeculotomy and study of reversible cupping. Ophthalmology 1982;89:219–26.
3. Anderson DR. Trabeculotomy compared to goniotomy for glaucoma in children. Ophthalmology 1983;90:805–6.
4. Burke JP, Bowell R. Primary trabeculectomy in congenital glaucoma. Br J Ophthalmol 1989;73:186–90.
5. Detry-Morel M, Feron EM. Trabeculectomy in congenital glaucoma: retrospective medium and long term results. Bull Soc Belge Ophtalmol 1996;262:143–51.
6. Fulcher T, Chan J, Lanigan B, et al. Long term follow up of primary trabeculectomy for infantile glaucoma. Br J Ophthalmol 1996;80:499–502.
7. Khaw PT. What is the best primary surgical treatment for the infantile glaucomas? (Editorial). Br J Ophthalmol 1996;80:495–6.
8. DeLuise VP, Anderson DR. Primary infantile glaucoma. Surv Ophthalmol 1983;28:1–19.

5 Non-Penetrating Surgery for Glaucoma

Juan Roberto Sampaolesi, MD
Roberto Sampaolesi, MD

Editor's Note: Professor Roberto Sampaolesi is one of the world's most widely recognized glaucoma experts. His knowledge is profound, his experience is extensive. His research is sound and highly productive. He is admired as a skilled physician, distinguished teacher, and eminent investigator and productive author.

Background

Goldmann, by means of manometric experiments carried out between 1946 and 1949, was the first to find the resistance site (R). Upon measuring the pressure at the level of the aqueous veins and inside Schlemm's canal, he found identical values. He also measured it in the anterior chamber and in the Schlemm's canal, where there was a marked and significance difference. Based on this he inferred that the site of the aqueous humor outflow resistance (R) was located between the anterior chamber and the Schlemm's canal, i.e. at the trabecular meshwork. Perkins (1953) concluded similarly and Sears (1964), by using a more sophisticated method, reported that the resistance site is located at the level of the Schlemm's canal.

Non-penetrating surgery is closely linked to Schlemm's canal surgery.

Our experience of several hundred surgical procedures in early congenital glaucomas within two years of age throughout 56 years of practice (Sampaolesi 1994) has given us the expertise necessary for the identification of Schlemm's canal. Trabeculotomy, even after the publications of Burian in 1960, Burian & Allen in 1962 and Sugar in 1961, was a difficult technique to master until 1968, when Cairns introduced trabeculectomy as a surgical technique for open-angle glaucoma.

It was Krasnov, in 1962, who originally proposed the removal of the external wall of the Schlemm's canal and coined the word sinusotomy for this procedure, by which he removed the external wall of Schlemm's canal; the inner wall of Schlemm's canal was untouched and then the conjunctiva was closed. However, this technique was not published until 1964. Alkseev (1978) proposed the removal of the endothelium of the inner wall of Schlemm's canal and of the juxtacanalicular tissue during sinusotomy, as this may increase the permeability of the inner wall of the sinus.

Zimmerman et al (1984) introduced non-penetrating trabeculectomy; Fyodorov et al (1984) proposed deep sclerectomy and later, and together with Kozlov and others (1989), non-penetrating deep sclerectomy; Kozlov et al (1990) improved the method with the addition of a cylindric collagen implant and later developed laser goniopuncture. In 1991, Arenas Archila proposed trabeculotomy ab externo, which removed the same tissues, after removing the external wall of Schlemm's canal, but using a microtrephine working at a speed of 800 rpm. In 1999 Stegmann reported his results with viscocanalostomy in black African patients. Sourdille et al (1999) used a triangular reticulated hyaluronic acid implant with the same dimensions as those of the second triangular scleral flap, which we have successfully tested.

Baseline and Follow-Up Examinations

All our patients underwent non-penetrating deep sclerectomy according to Kozlov's technique, with the use of Minsky's transillumination technique, by which all the components of the chamber angle become evident, thus allowing proper placement of the incision.

The evolution was monitored pre- and postoperatively at 6-month-intervals by means of single-spot checks and daily pressure curves (Sampaolesi, 1961; Sampaolesi and Reca, 1964 and Sampaolesi, Calixto, Carvalho and Reca, 1968); the optic nerve condition was assessed by means of confocal tomography (Heidelberg Retina Tomograph: HRT) and compared to the normal and pathological tomographic values for each parameter according to our guidelines (Sampaolesi R and Sampaolesi JR, 1999), while the flow was measured with Doppler by using the HRF (Heidelberg Retina Flowmeter). Finally, the visual field was evaluated with computerized perimetry (Octopus 101, program G2 and Peri-Data software).

Surgical Technique

A rectangular one-third scleral thickness limbal-based scleral flap, the same as that created for a trabeculectomy, is dissected. One side of this rectangle, of 5 mm, is parallel to the limbus, while another one is perpendicular to it and 6 mm in length. Anteriorly, the scleral flap is dissected closer to the cornea than usual in trabeculectomy procedures. Corneal lamellae are dissected along 1.5 mm.

A second limbal-based triangular scleral flap is then created by penetrating 1,5 mm along the corneal tissue. A useful landmark for this dissection, which must be performed carefully, is the orientation of the scleral fibers, which though arranged in multiple directions at the scleral level, behind this flap, they become neatly parallel and circular at the level of the scleral spur, thus adopting a more whitish and nacreous appearance. Aqueous humor percolation at this stage, with the anterior chamber closed, when the dissection goes from the scleral spur towards the cornea, is indicative of placement of the incision at the proper plane. The triangular flap, containing the external wall of the Schlemm's canal, including its endothelium, is then resected. Anteriorly, the dissection should be made down to the deep corneal lamellae so that only the corneal endothelium, Descemet's membrane and a small layer of corneal lamellae are left. The dissection plane can generally be easily created at this final stage by pulling the vertex of the triangular flap towards the cornea with a clamp.

Once the triangular flap has been removed, the surgeon resects a membrane formed by the inner wall of Schlemm's canal with its endothelium, the juxtacanalicular tissue and the external corneoscleral trabecular meshwork, while both internal corneoscleral trabecular meshwork and uveal trabecular meshwork remain intact, attached to the Descemet's membrane and the corneal endothelium. These tissues which remain intact constitute the so-called trabeculo-descemet's membrane, which is so resistant that it keeps the anterior chamber formed, avoids ocular hypertension and spares the complications of trabeculectomy.

The next step involves placement of the hydrophylic implant, either the cylindrical one or the triangular one, which is secured by placing a nylon 10/0 suture, followed by closure of the conjunctival flap with two stitches, and of the conjunctiva at the level of the corneoscleral limbus.

The description above depicts what happens when the procedure is performed by an experienced surgeon. Otherwise, it is very important for the inexperienced surgeon to correlate what he sees in the surgical field with its anatomical elements.

Anatomic and Histologic Considerations in the Surgical Technique

Figure 1 is a schematic representation of the chamber angle. The sclera ends anteriorly with three prongs: two long ones, one anterior, which forms the sclero-corneal limbus and one posterior one, which forms the scleral septum. Its anterior edge is Schwalbe's line. The third prong is shorter and constitutes the scleral spur. The two first ones form an optic canal which lodges the cornea, while between the second and the third one a filtration canal is formed to lodge the Schlemm's canal and the trabecular meshwork.

If the dissection has been performed correctly, the image on **Figure 2**, showing three clear areas is visualized. The limbar area, area 1, is dark. The last iris rolls can be seen by transparency through the endothelium and Descemet's membrane if, according to Minsky's maneuver, the area is transilluminated by means of the optical fiber of the microscope supported by the cornea, and separated from it by one of the white triangles used for drying, but embedded in physiological solution to prevent the cornea from overheating.

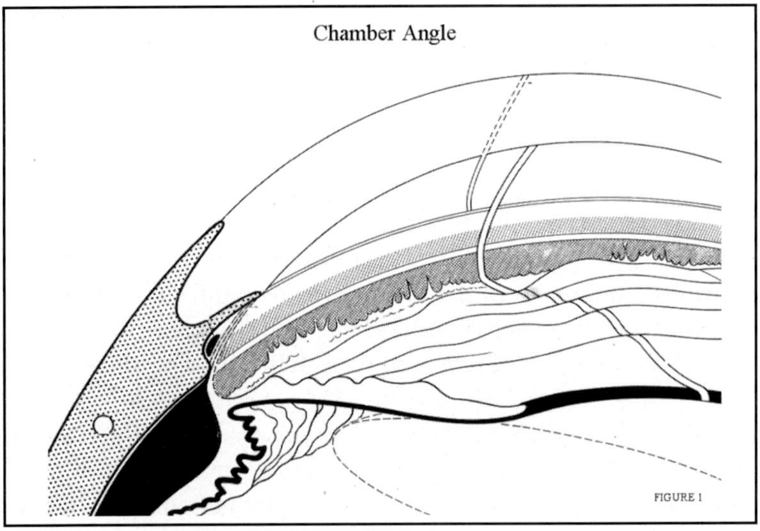

Figure 1: Schematic representation of the chamber angle. The sclera ends anteriorly with three prongs: two long ones, one anterior, which forms the sclerocorneal limbus and one posterior one, which forms the scleral septum. Its anterior edge is Schwalbe's line. The third prong is shorter and constitutes the scleral spur. The two first ones form an optic canal which lodges the cornea, while between the second and the third one a filtration canal is formed to lodge the Schlemm's canal and the trabecular meshwork.

Area 2 can be identified by its blue color, it is located more backwards and called blue area. The anterior limit of this area corresponds with Schwalbe's line, which anatomically constitutes the anterior edge of the scleral septum, while the posterior limit of this blue area corresponds with the scleral spur, with the Schlemm's canal located anteriorly. The third area, located behind the blue one, is white-grayish (as the ciliary muscle is visualized by transparency) and triangular, and made up of scleral tissue covering the external surface of the ciliary muscle.

Figure 3 includes **Figure 2** at its center and on the right, and a photograph of the surgery when the second triangular scleral flap is removed, has been placed on the left. On this flap removed, the hazel- or brown-colored granulous sector observed is the external wall of Schlemm's canal, from which some drops of aqueous humor are seen flowing smoothly.

The anatomo-pathologic examination of the triangular flap resected shows some corneal lamellae and the endothelium of the external wall of Schlemm's canal (**Figure 4 A**). The flat preparation of **Figure 4 B** shows the endothelial nuclei of the external wall of Schlemm's canal.

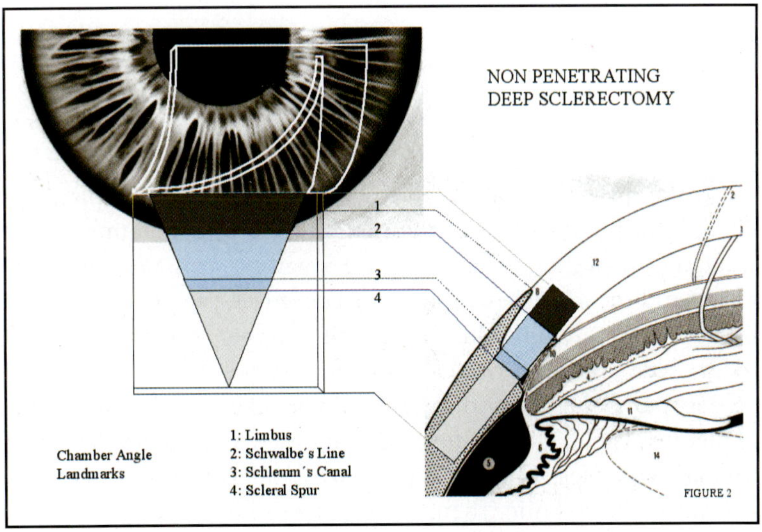

Figure 2: The dissection has been correctly performed if three clear areas are visualized. Dark area (limbar area). Blue area 2 (more posterior), with its anterior limit corresponding to Schwalbe's line, and its posterior limit, to the scleral spur and the open Schlemm's canal. White-grayish area 3 (behind the blue area), triangular, made up of scleral tissue and covering the external surface of the ciliary muscle. On the right side of this figure the correspondence of the surgical appearance of the three areas with the anatomic elements of the chamber angle can be seen.

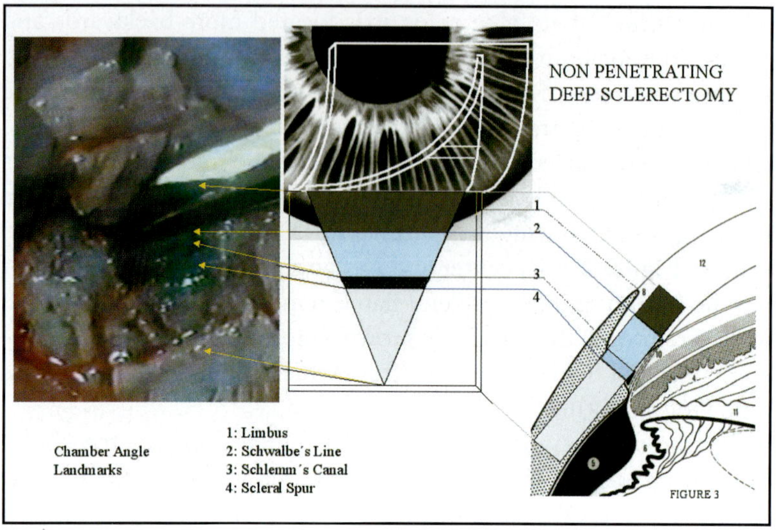

Figure 3: Removal of the second triangular scleral flap (left), on which the external wall of Schlemm's canal, identified by its hazel- or brown-colored granulous appearance, can be seen. Center and right: correlation of this photograph with the landmarks of figure 2.

If the dissection has failed to be done at the correct plane and it is not deep enough for the resection of the external wall of Schlemm's canal by means of the triangular flap, the image of **Figure 5** will be seen, i.e., the dark area 1, the blue area 2 and the grayish-white area 3; moreover, the open Schlemm's canal will not be seen in area 2, light blue. Should this happen, special attention should be given to the blue area, and the fact that Schwalbe's line is the anterior limit and the scleral spur is the posterior one should be taken into account. The external wall of Schlemm's canal, located at the darkest blue area adjacent to the posterior line of the blue area (scleral spur) **(Figure 6)** should thus be dissected with fine clamps and with a sharp knife. Then, some aqueous humor drops will smoothly come out. Adjacent to the scleral spur (number 4 in the figure), there is a definite darker area, also blue, corresponding to the Schlemm's canal and represented in the figure by number 3.

Figures 7 A and **B** illustrate the dissection of the external wall of Schlemm's canal under direct illumination (a) and under transillumination (b), done with an instrument specially designed for this purpose by Grieshaber.

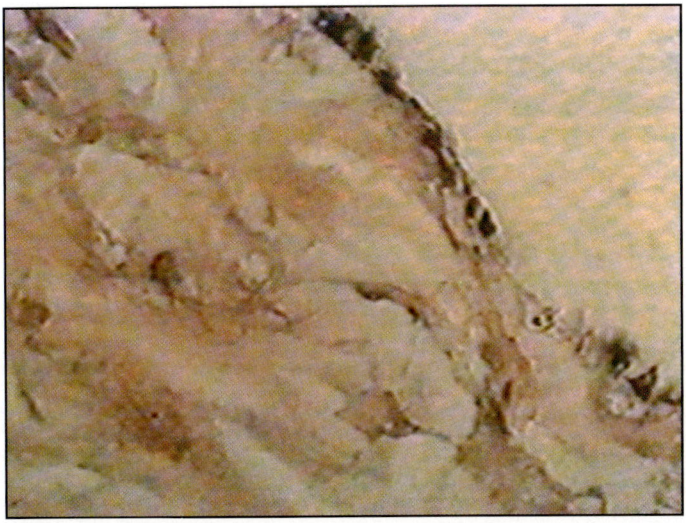

Figure 4 A: Anatomo-pathologic examination of the triangular flap showing some corneal lamellae and the endothelium of the external wall of Schlemm's canal.

Figure 4 B: Endothelial nuclei of the external wall of Schlemm's canal (flat preparation).

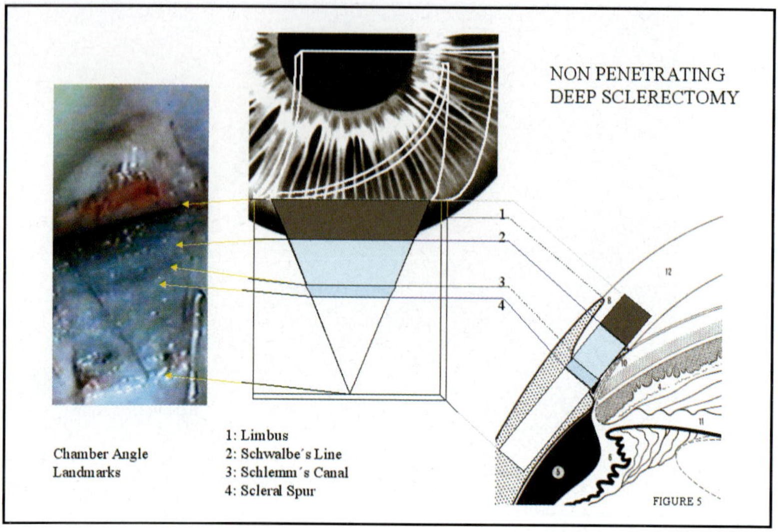

Figure 5: Image visualized if the dissection has failed to be done at the correct plane and it is not deep enough for the resection of the external wall of the Schlemm's canal by means of the triangular flap. All three areas are visible but the open Schlemm's canal is not (left). The schematic representation at the center shows the key element for the surgeon to find the Schlemm's canal: the most posterior darker blue sector (between 3 and 4) of the blue area corresponds to the Schlemm's canal.

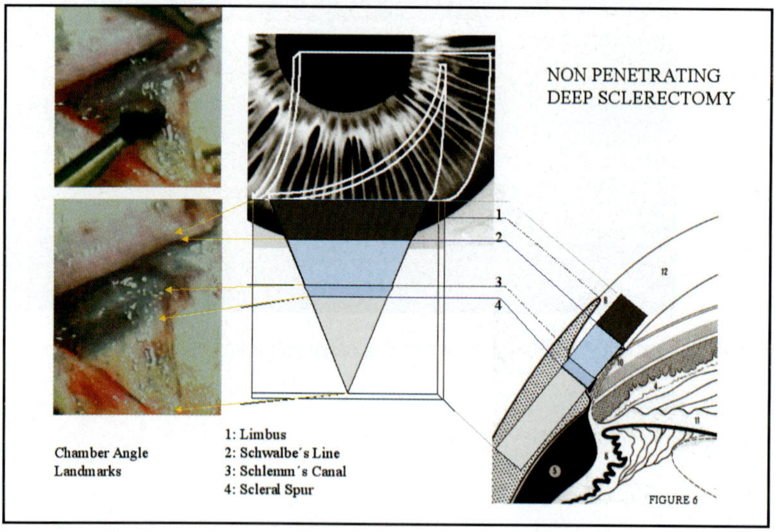

Figure 6: The most important surgical step is to open Schlemm's canal, located at the posterior part of the blue area, adjacent to the scleral spur.

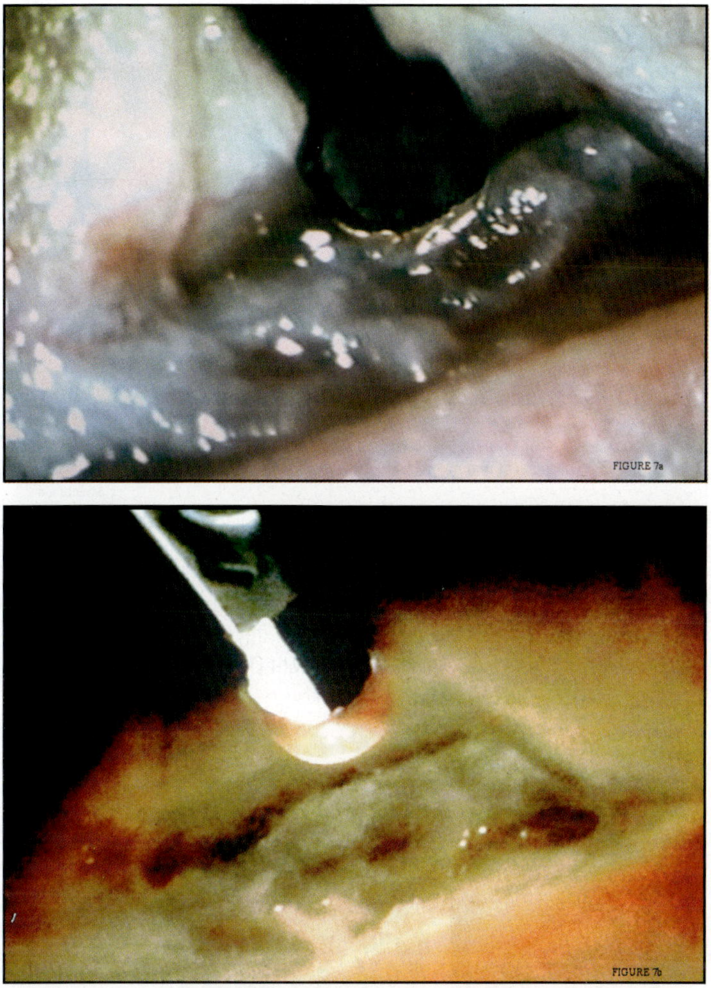

Figure 7: Dissection of the external wall of the Schlemm's canal under direct illumination (a) and under transillumination (b), done with an instrument specially designed for this purpose by Grieshaber.

Figure 8 shows the dissection of the internal wall of Schlemm's canal with its endothelium, juxtacanalicular tissue and the external corneoscleral trabecular meshwork. On the right-bottom there is a schematic representation of the tissue removed and of its previous locations, where only the internal corneoscleral trabecular meshwork and the uveal trabecular meshwork, which, together with Descemet's membrane form the trabeculo-descemet's membrane, are left.

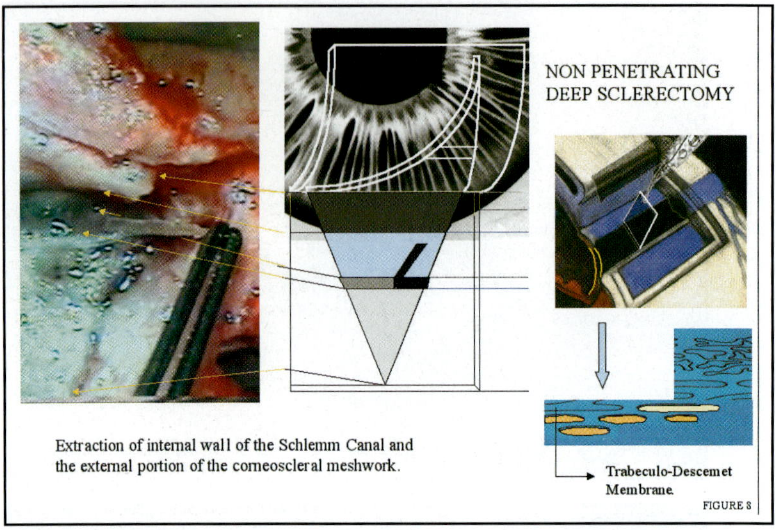

Figure 8: Dissection of the inner wall of Schlemm's canal with its endothelium, juxtacanalicular tissue and the external corneoscleral trabecular meshwork (left). Schematic representation of the tissue removed and of its previous locations (center), where only the internal corneoscleral trabecular meshwork and the uveal trabecular meshwork, which, together with Descemet's membrane form the trabeculo-descemet's membrane, are left (bottom-right).

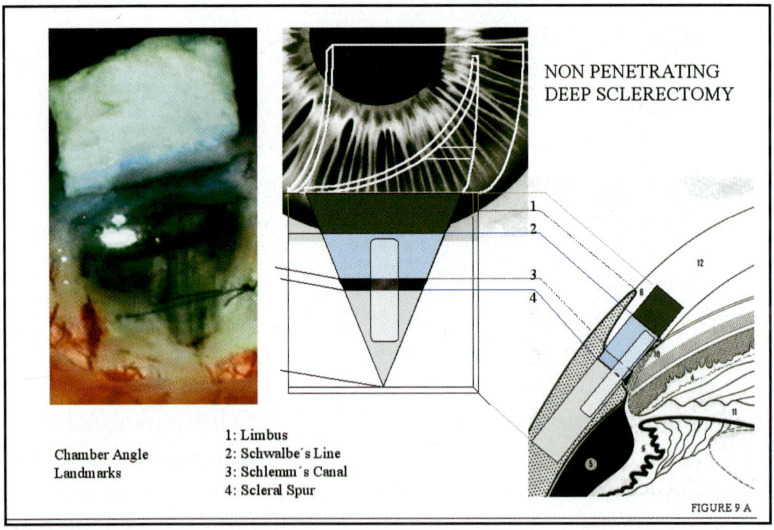

Figure 9A: Correctly placed implant (photograph taken during the surgical procedure).

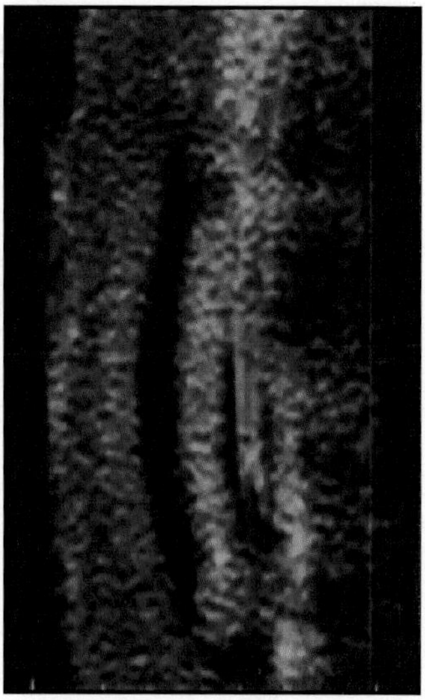

Figure 9B: Ultrasound biomicroscopy showing, from left to right: conjunctival tissue with aqueous humor, separating it from the cuadrangular scleral flap and two parallel lines behind it corresponding to the implant, where the nylon suture securing it can be seen. The implant is surrounded by aqueous humor and the scleral lake is seen behind it.

Figure 9A is a photograph taken during the surgical procedure showing the implant correctly placed and secured with a nylon 10/0 suture. Correct placement of the implant can be verified by ultrasound biomicroscopy (**Figure 9B**).

This correlation was the same when we used Harms and Paufique's trabeculotomy technique **(Figure 10)**. After creating the square scleral flap, when we opened the incision performed perpendicular to the limbus in order to find Schlemm's canal, a superior dark triangle corresponding to the lumen of the open Schlemm's canal and an inferior whitish triangle corresponding to the sclera covering the anterior surface of the ciliary muscle, could be seen through the oval thus created. A white-nacreous line corresponding to the circular fibers of the scleral spur was also seen between both triangles. The trabeculotome is introduced in the superior triangle, first on the right and then on the left, in order to perform the trabeculotomy.

In children, if the procedure has been done properly, a little hyphema reaching out to the pupil but not surpassing its borders should be seen **(Figure 11)**. This hyphema is caused by the rupture of the artery of Schlemm's canal, which is known as Friedenwald's artery. Should a large hyphema filling the whole anterior chamber develop, it would indicate that a cyclodyalisis has been done instead of a trabeculotomy.

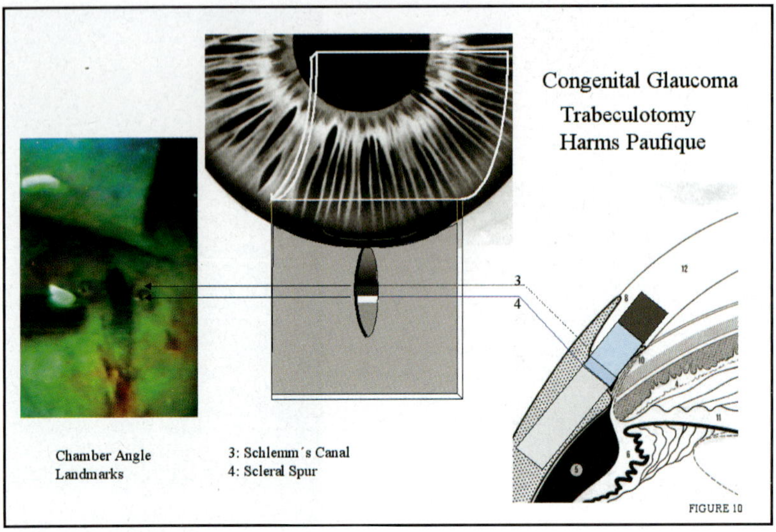

Figure 10: Same correlation with Harms and Paufique's trabeculotomy technique. The most important element to be identified is the scleral spur. After creating the cuadrangular flap by which the scleral thickness is reduced, an incision is performed perpendicular to the limbus. When this incision is open, a black triangle is visible beside the limbus, followed by a gray-nacreous triangle, on the vertix of which there is a white-nacreous area corresponding to the scleral spur (4). The trabeculotome is introduced parallel to the limbus in the dark triangle, adjacent to the scleral spur. Left: photograph taken during the procedure. Right: anatomic correlation.

Upon gonioscopy performed 1 week after trabeculotomy, blood is seen coming from the Schlemm's canal to the anterior chamber through the opening performed on the Schlemm's canal **(Figure 12)**.

Results

The intraocular pressure was successfully regulated in 85 % of cases, with 10 cases requiring Yag Laser at the level of Schwalbe's line, cornea and trabecular meshwork, according to Mermoud's technique (Mermoud et al 1999). With the addition of topical therapy with eyedrops, a success rate of 95 % was achieved.

The pre- and postoperative IOP values were 28.2 mmHg ± 7 mmHg and 13 mmHg ± 7 mmHg respectively, according to single-spot checks. In all cases in which the IOP was regulated, the daily pressure curve consistently revealed mean values not exceeding 20 mmHg and a variability (standard deviation) lower than 2.1 mmHg. The daily pressure curves performed preoperatively yielded the following overall results: Mean (M): 24 mmHg; Variability (V): 2.6 and the postoperative values were 15.8 mmHg and 2.0 respectively.

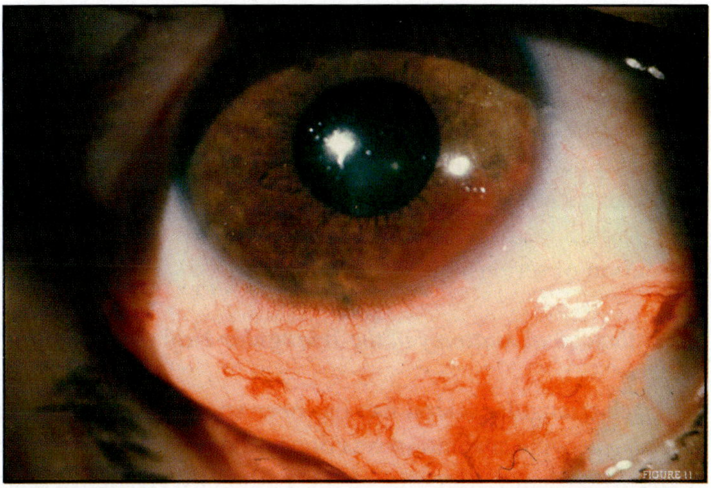

Figure 11: Very small hyphema extending to but not surpassing the pupillary border. This may occur in children after trabeculotomy, if the procedure has been done correctly.

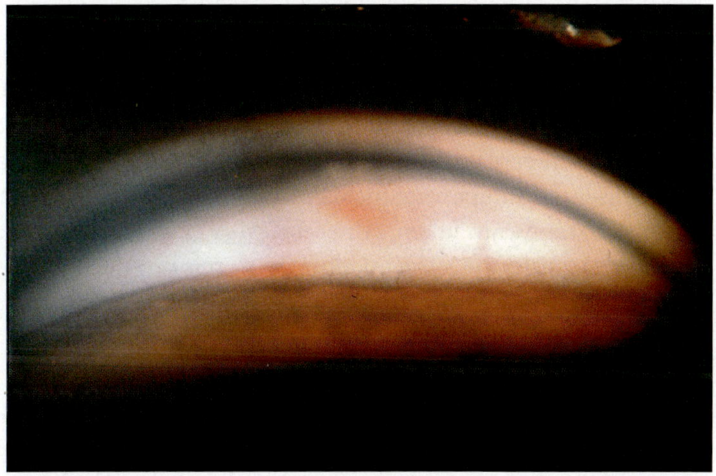

Figure 12: Postoperative gonioscopy showing blood coming from Schlemm's canal extending to the anterior chamber through the opening of Schlemm's canal.

The main advantage of this technique is the high percentage of cases in which it prevents the three most severe complications of trabeculectomy: flat chamber, hyphema and choroidal detachment. Furthermore, since neither anterior chamber opening nor iridectomy or atropine instillation into the anterior chamber are required, the postoperative period is good, with the patient preserving the preoperative visual acuity, while our experience with trabeculectomy has shown us an otherwise difficult postoperative course, independently of the success of the procedure.

Moreover, the mild postoperative period, as well as the low percentage of complications has encouraged surgeons to safely recommend this technique as early as in the pre-perimetric period, when damage to the optic nerve has already occurred and pharmacotherapy has failed to regulate IOP, though visual acuity and visual field are still normal. This technique is thus pretty close to the ideal therapy for the prevention of serious anatomic and functional damage caused by the disease.

Pathological Anatomy of the Triangular Flap Technique

Each triangular scleral flap has been studied both macro- and microscopically. The macroscopic evaluation was done according to the surface technique reported at the Microscopy Meeting of the Pathology Academy (Zarate 1999), which is based on two main principles involved in the inclusion process: firstly, transparency of the specimen after passing it through xylol and secondly, application of Scheimpflug's principle by which an excellent resolution at different planes can be obtained.

The biopsies were fixed in buffer 10 % phormol to be later dehydrated in three stages, in the first two stages in 96 % alcohol for 10 hours each and in 100 % alcohol in the last stage. Finally, they are placed in xylol for three hours. Then, when each specimen is placed on a slide, the endothelial surface should be marked as a tip for orientation upon its inclusion in paraffin. The specimen is cut by freezing and photographs are taken as necessary. A tiny cut at the vertex of the triangle located nearest to the surgeon, done with scissors during surgery upon removing the flap, is very useful for the pathologist to handle it safely.

Results

Deep sclerectomy specimens have an irregular architecture towards the edges, in contrast to those from ordinary trabeculectomies. The internal surface of the external wall of Schlemm's canal can be identified by the clearly visible nuclei of the endothelium, and pigmented areas are usually seen as well. The histologic section of figure 4a shows a dense connective tissue wall adopting a pink acidophilic color when stained with hematoxylin-eosin, as well as a sector lined with endothelial cells of an enlarged shape forming a single coat of tightly attached cells which constitutes the endothelium of the external wall of Schlemm's canal. Nuclei are typically oval-shaped and they have soft cromatin. The scleral connective tissue shows fibroblasts which are irregularly spread along the collagen. The flat preparation of figure 4 b shows the nuclei of the endothelial cells of the inner surface of Schlemm's canal.

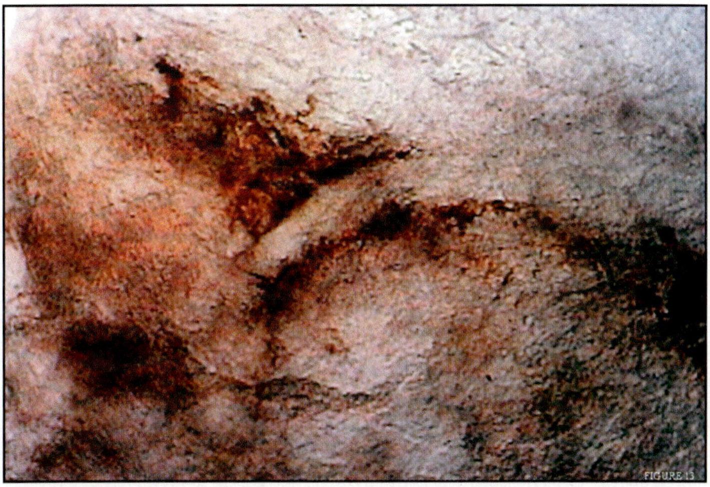

Figure 13: Flat preparation showing a collector coming into the Schlemm's canal.

Figure 13 illustrates a flat preparation showing a collector entering Schlemm's canal.

Nd:YAG Laser Goniopuncture

In 20 % of cases, YAG goniopuncture was required between months 1 to 5 postoperatively for IOP regulation in cases reaching as high as 20 mmHg or more according to a single-spot check, or in the presence of pathologic results revealed by a daily pressure curve. The lens designed by Rousell and Fankhauser and manufactured by Haag Streit was used for this procedure. The aim was to perforate the resistance zone if surgery had failed to remove part of the corresponding tissue, and thereby communicate the anterior chamber with the scleral lake or the subconjunctival space. The aiming beam is focused on the trabeculo-descemet's membrane with a power of 2 to 3.5 mJ; however, sometimes, higher power, 4 to 5 mJ is required, but it should be kept in mind that a power above 4 mJ may cause small hemorrhages which can be stopped by strongly pressing the lens against the eye. A total of 5 to 20 shots should be made at the level of Schwalbe's line, as well as above and below it. Digital massage, which is usually indicated after trabeculectomy, is wholly contraindicated in these cases. However, more experienced surgeons have concluded this YAG goniopuncture to be necessary in 48 % of cases (Mermoud).

Chamber Angle and Non-Penetrating Deep Sclerectomy

The chamber angle is a key factor when making the decision whether to perform NPDS, since this procedure is contraindicated in narrow-angle or angle-closure glaucomas, as it is in neovascular glaucomas, in cases with newly-formed membranes covering the trabecular meshwork zone after some trabeculoplasty procedures (Sampaolesi and Koller et al) and in congenital glaucomas with both types of angles: type I: pathological mesodermal remnants reaching out to or surpassing Schwalbe's line, and type II: apparent high insertion of the iris.

This procedure is suitably indicated in primary open-angle glaucoma, capsular glaucoma, pigmentary glaucoma, traumatic glaucoma, etc. It has been widely accepted that 40 % of cases of POAG in young patients (30 to 50 years of age) have goniodysgenesis characterized by the presence of pathological mesodermal remnants (Kniestedt, Gloor et al, 2000). These remnants may reach as far as the spur, the trabecular meshwork or Schwalbe's line. This is associated with a peripherally atrophic iris mesodermal superficial layer with black triangles visible at its periphery (pigmentary layer) formed between the radial vascular cords. The radial vessels and the iris greater arterial circle are also seen. Additionally, there is absence of ciliary body band, which is covered by pathological mesodermal remnants.

However, NPDS is indicated in these cases when the pathological mesodermal remnants do not surpass the scleral spur.

Figure 14A shows a case of glaucoma with exfoliation syndrome where there is the typical wave-like pigment line on the posterior surface of the cornea (Sampaolesi's line) at the sloping part of the chamber angle between 3 and 9 o'clock, going through the 6 o'clock position. This sign is important for early diagnosis of the syndrome before the typical signs develop on the pupil. In a population of 110 cases (Sampaolesi, 1959), 62 had the classical signs, whereas 50 cases were diagnosed based only on the presence of the typical waves, though the classical signs were absent. According to Mizuno (1977), Sampaolesi's line is observed in 94 % of cases presenting with the typical signs and in 82 % of those in which these signs are absent. **Figure 14B** illustrates an exfoliation syndrome case with mesodermal dysgenesis. Pigmentary glaucoma is a late congenital glaucoma (Malbran, 1957) and it is therefore associated with goniodysgenesis. **Figure 15A**

shows the typical image of a very dark, almost black, Schlemm's canal (1 in the figure), absent ciliary body band, which is covered with pathological mesodermal remnants (2), peripheral atrophy of the superficial mesodermal layer of the iris (2 to 4) by which the dark triangles corresponding to the pigmentary epithelium (3) become visible, and vascular cords with radial vessels (4). These last features

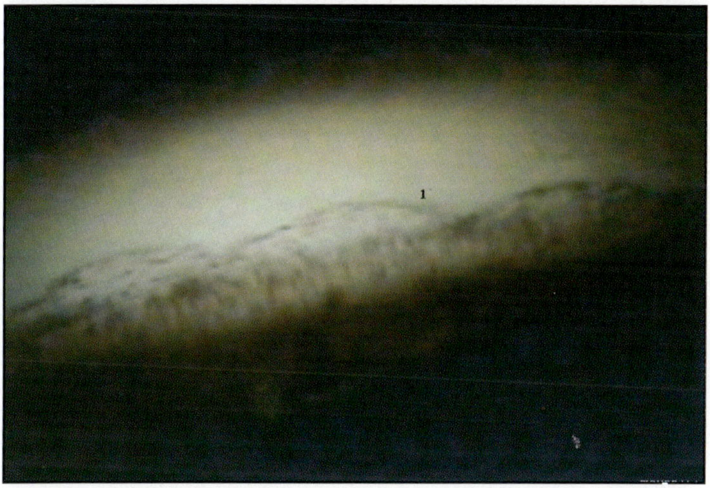

Figure 14 A: Glaucoma with Exfoliation Syndrome. The typical wave-like pigment line on the posterior surface of the cornea (1-Sampaolesi's line) at the sloping part of the chamber angle between 3 and 9 o'clock, going through the 6 o'clock position in a case of glaucoma with exfoliation syndrome.

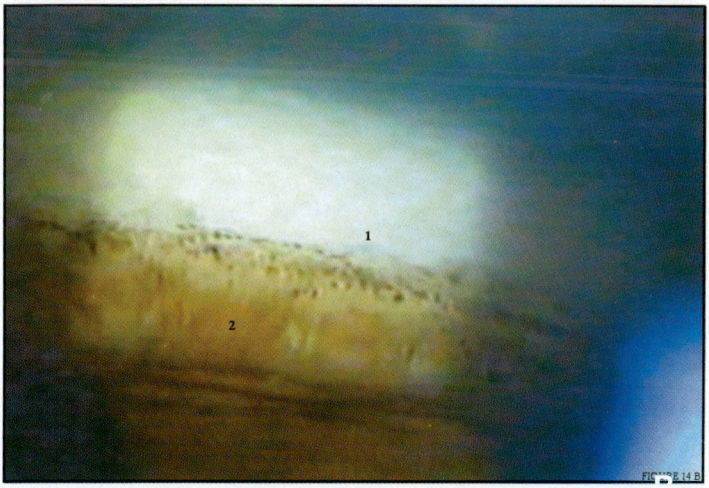

Figure 14 B: Exfoliation syndrome with mesodermal dysgenesis.

are typical in goniodysgenesis. **Figure 15B** shows another case where the iris atrophy is not marked, while the presence of very thick pathological mesodermal remnants (1), covering the ciliary body band, is clearly visible. The last iris roll is indicated with number 2, the highly pigmented Schlemm's canal, with number 3, and Schwalbe's line, with number 4.

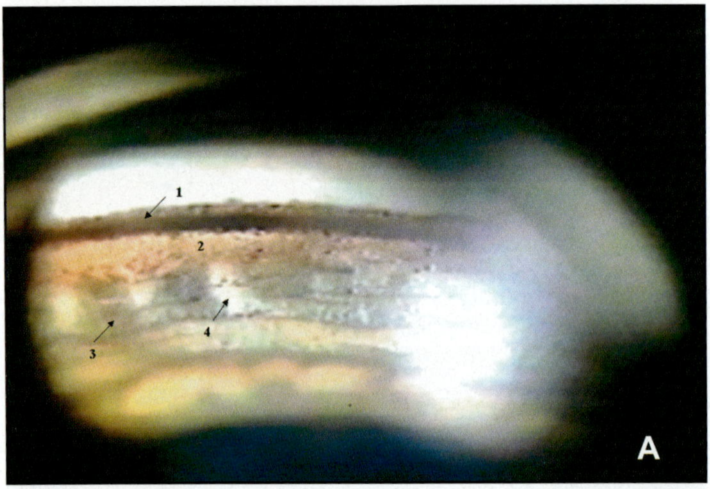

Figure 15 A: Goniodysgenesis. Very dark, almost black, Schlemm's canal (1), absent ciliary body band, which is covered with pathological mesodermal remnants (2), peripheral atrophy of the superficial mesodermal layer of the iris (2 to 4) by which the dark triangles corresponding to the pigmentary epithelium (3) become visible, and vascular cords with radial vessels (4). These last features are typical in goniodysgenesis.

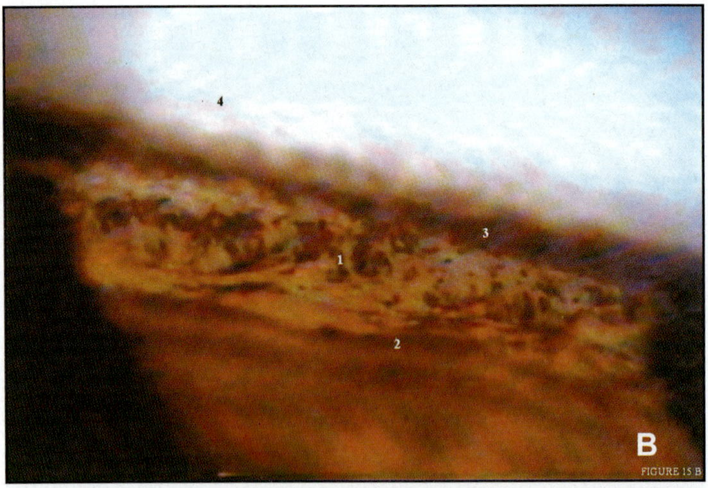

Figure 15 B: Another case where the iris atrophy is not marked, while the presence of very thick pathological mesodermal remnants (1), covering the ciliary body band, is clearly visible. 2: last iris roll, 3: highly pigmented Schlemm's canal, 4: Schwalbe's line.

Figure 16 shows a goniodysgenesis, without pigmentary glaucoma, where the pathological mesodermal remnants cover the ciliary body band completely.

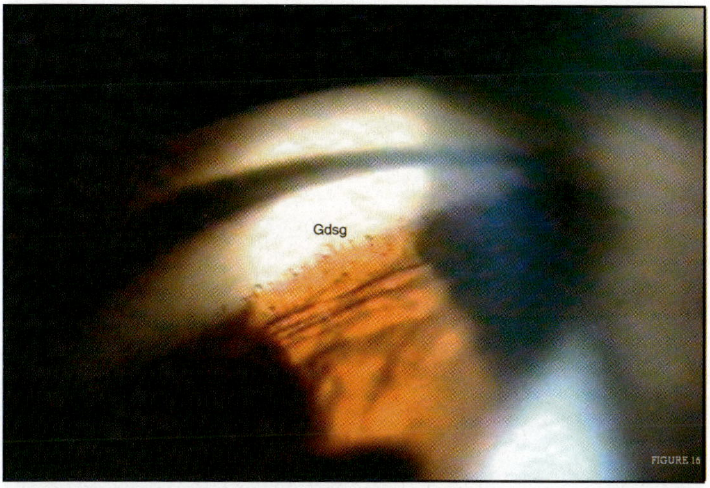

Figure 16: Goniodysgenesis without pigmentary glaucoma. The pathological mesodermal remnants cover the ciliary body band completely.

Gonioscopy after Non-Penetrating Deep Sclerectomy (NPDS)

Figures 17 A and **B** illustrate the typical appearance of the chamber angle after NPDS. The dark area (a) on the external wall of the chamber angle is the scleral lake (1 in the figure), which can be clearly seen full of liquid with a fine slit cut (b). Both figures show the Schlemm's canal and the trabecular meshwork which have become convex, raised towards the interior of the anterior chamber, because they have been displaced, and therefore, deformed, by the cylindrical implant.

Figures 18 A and **B** show another appearance of the chamber angle after this procedure. In a it looks as if the procedure has been penetrating, however, if viewed in a fine slit cut (b), a very thin trabeculo-descemet's membrane is seen.

Figure 19 shows the accidental perforation of the trabeculo-descemet's membrane during the procedure.

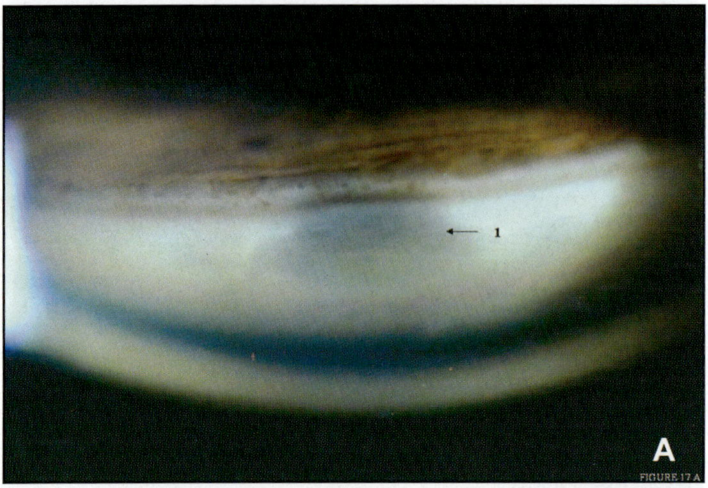

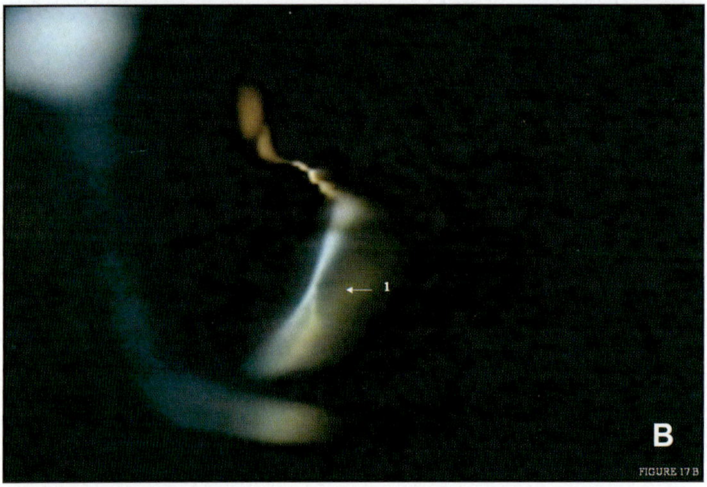

Figure 17 A and B: Typical appearance of the chamber angle after NPDS. The Schlemm's canal and the trabecular meshwork have become convex, raised towards the interior of the anterior chamber, because they have been displaced by the cylindrical implant, which deforms them. In a, the dark area seen by difuse illumination on the external wall of the chamber angle is the scleral lake (1), which, in b, it is seen full of liquid with a fine slit cut.

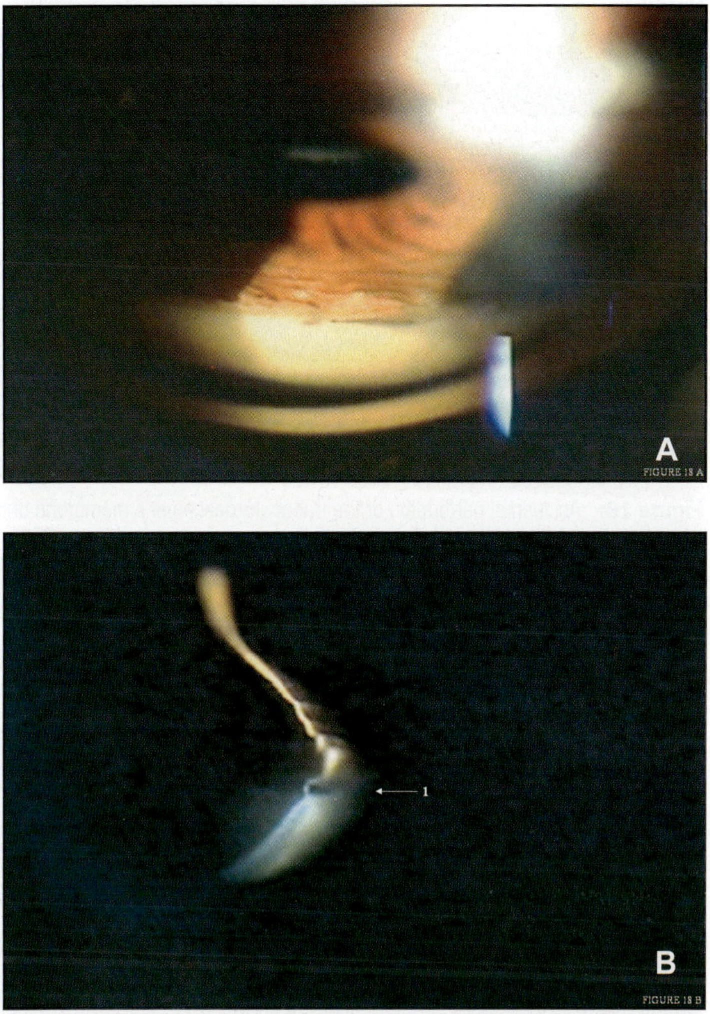

Figure 18 A and B: Another appearance of the chamber angle after this procedure. In (a) it looks as if the procedure has been penetrating, however, if viewed in a fine slit cut (b), a very thin trabeculo-descemet's membrane is seen.

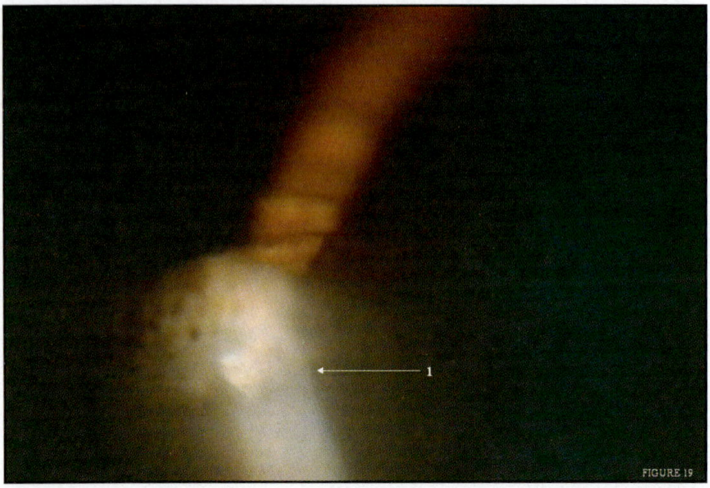

Figure 19: Accidental perforation of the trabeculo-descemet's membrane during the procedure.

Figure 20: Absence of the uveal trabecular meshwork, of the external corneoscleral trabecular meshwork and of the juxtacanalicular tissue after a Yag-laser procedure. This area is limited by two white cords: Schwalbe's line (1) and scleral spur (2) and it is usually filled with blood (3), which comes into the anterior chamber, as it occurs in congenital glaucomas after trabeculotomy. Bleeding is stopped by slightly pressing the lens.

Figure 20 shows the absence of the uveal trabecular meshwork, of the external corneoscleral trabecular meshwork and of the juxtacanalicular tissue after a Yag-laser procedure. This area is limited by two white cords: Schwalbe's line (1) and scleral spur (2) and it is usually filled with blood (3), which comes into the anterior chamber, as it occurs in congenital glaucomas after trabeculotomy. Bleeding is stopped by slightly pressing the lens.

Other Non-Penetrating Procedures

In addition to NPDS, other techniques have been used and, though considered to be non-penetrating, they sometimes feature small perforations, such as Stegmann's viscocanalostomy **(Figure 21)**. The first steps of this technique are the same as those for NPDS, but the external wall of Schlemm's canal is removed with the second flap, while the inner wall is left intact. Viscoelastic substance, which is then injected through both orifices of Schlemm's canal, clears the aqueous humor outflow pathways from Schlemm's canal onwards. Anatomo-pathologic studies performed by Johnson and Johnson (2000) on human eyes after viscocanalostomy revealed that the external wall of Schlemm's canal was open at the area closest to Schwalbe's line.

In another technique created by Burk, Hydrotrabeculotomy **(Figure 22)**, the first steps are also the same as in NPDS, but, a channeled Geuder trabeculotome through which serum can be introduced by pressure, perforates the inner wall of Schlemm's canal and the trabecular meshwork, thus penetrating into the anterior chamber. This technique is actually perforating, although the anterior chamber is not emptied. When we used this technique, a small intraoperative hyphema not reaching the pupil was observed.

Burk has presented laser trabeculotomy **(Figure 23)**. The laser rays emitted towards the anterior chamber by a small gold angled mirror attached to the trabeculotome perforate the inner wall of the Schlemm's canal and the trabecular meshwork up to the chamber angle, as seen in the scanning electron microscopy at the bottom of the figure (white arrows).

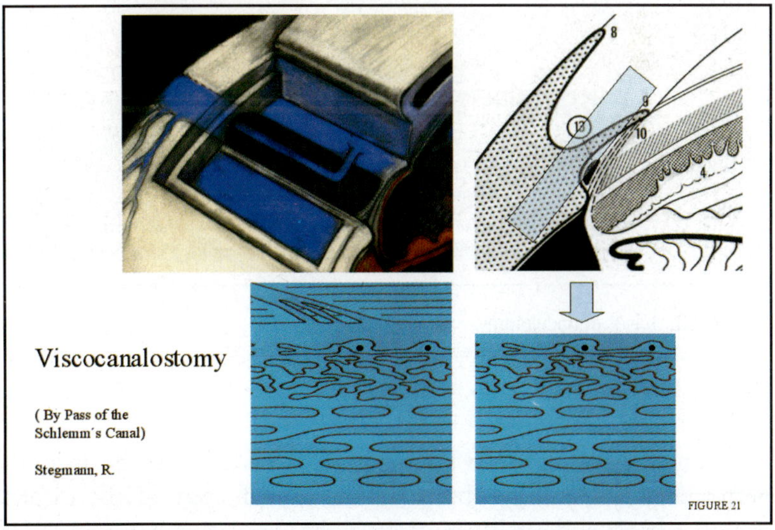

Figure 21: Stegmann's viscocanalostomy.

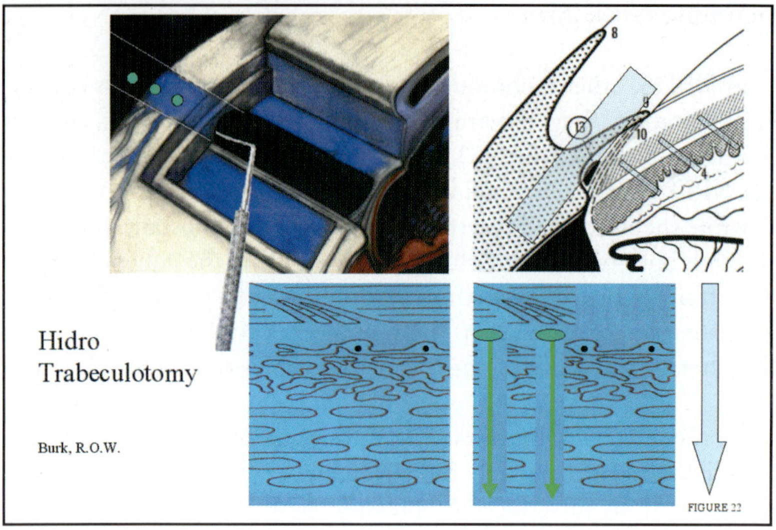

Figure 22: Hydrotrabeculotomy.

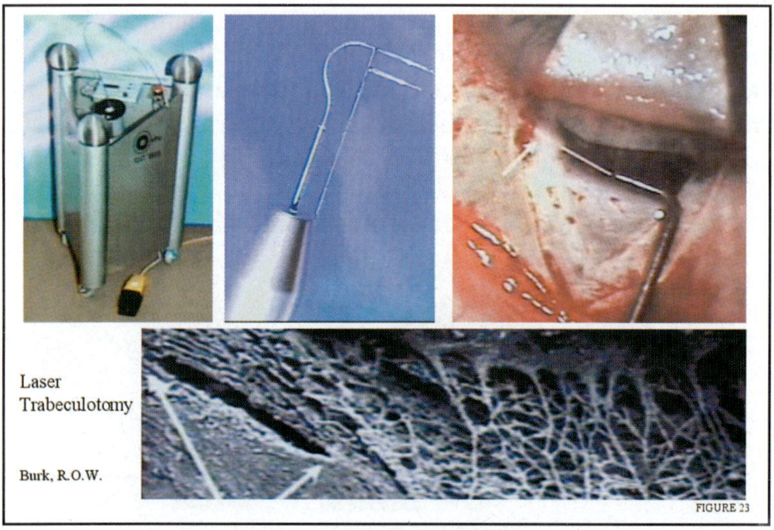

Figure 23: Laser trabeculotomy.

Discussion

Non-penetrating deep sclerectomy, provided that the technique is properly performed, by carefully observing the morphology of the external wall of the chamber angle and establishing the right correlation between the elements of the external wall of the chamber angle at the three zones visualized by the surgeon after the dissection of the deep triangular flap, should lead to the successful removal of the external wall of Schlemm's canal as well as its inner wall with the juxtacanalicular tissue and the external corneoscleral meshwork.

Throughout our experience, this technique has proven to be similarly effective in IOP regulation as trabeculectomy.

By postoperative ultrasound biomicroscopic examination correct placement of the implant is verified. This technique also reveals the presence of aqueous humor in the subscleral lake and, in some cases, its outflow through the unconventional uveoscleral pathway **(Figure 9B)**.

The typical complications of trabeculectomy, such as athalamia, hyphema and choroidal detachment, have barely occurred. Moreover, and among the advantages of this technique, the fact that no anterior chamber opening, iridectomy or use of mydriatics are required, as well as the good evolution, with recovery of the preoperative visual acuity as early as on the first postoperative day, should be mentioned.

Its safety and immediate good postoperative evolution warrant the indication of surgery as early as in the pre-perimetric period of glaucoma, when medication fails to regulate the IOP and in the presence of optic nerve damage as revealed by the HRT, when both visual acuity and visual field are normal, thus becoming a useful and more efficient tool which can help glaucomatous patients prevent the serious damage caused by this disease to the optic nerve, and, consequently, to the visual field.

Editorial Comment

It is important to mention that several prospective randomized trials have been conducted to compare the efficacy and side effects profile of non-penetrating surgery with that of trabeculectomy. [Jonescu-Cuypers C, Jacobi P, Konen W, et al. Primary viscocanalostomy versus trabeculectomy in white patients with open-angle glaucoma: a randomized clinical trial. Ophthalmology 2001;108: 254–8]. Although these trials were mostly of limited follow-up, they did generally demonstrate that postoperative IOP reduction was equivalent or slightly worse compared with that of trabeculectomy, but with less frequency of complications.

Samuel Boyd, MD. Editor-in-Chief.

Acknowledgment

The authors want to thank Prof. Dr. Jorge Oscar Zarate for his contributions on pathology.

This chapter was supported by a grant of "Fundación Argentina Oftalmológica Dr. Juan Sampaolesi".

Bibliography

1. Alekseev BN (1978): Microsurgery of the internal wall of Schlemm's canal. Vestn Oftal 4: 4-14.
2. Arenas Archila E (1991): Trabeculectomy ab externo. Highlights Ophthalmol Lett XIX: 9.
3. Bechetoille A (2000): In Krieglstein GK: Glaucoma Update VI. Pro Edit, Heidelberg: 97.
4. Burian HM & Allen L (1962): Trabeculotomy ab externo. A new glaucoma operation: technique and results of experimental surgery. Amer J Ophthalmol 53: 19-26.
5. Burian HM (1960): A case of Marfan's syndrome with bilateral glaucoma. With description of a new type of operation for developmental glaucoma (trabeculotomy ab externo). Amer J Ophthalmol 50: 1187-1192.
6. Burk R.O.W. (2001): First International Congress on non-penetrating Glaucoma Surgery, February 1-2, 2001, Lausanne, Switzerland. Abstract Book.
7. Cairns JE (1968): Trabeculectomy; preliminary report of a new method. Amer J Ophthalmol 66: 673.
8. Demailly P, Jeanteur-Lunel MN, Berkani M et al (1996): Non penetrating deep sclerectomy associated with collagen device in primary open angle glaucoma: middle-term retrospective study. J Fr Ophtalmol 19: 659-666.
9. Fyodorov SN et al (1984): Deep sclerectomy: technique and mechanism of a new glaucomatous procedure. Glaucoma 6: 281-283.
10. Fyodorov SN et al.(1989): Non-penetrating deep sclerectomy in open-angle glaucoma. IRTC Eye Microsurgery. RSFSR Ministry of Public Health, Moscow: 52-55.
11. Goldmann H (1946): Drainage of aqueous in man. Ophthalmologica 112: 11-146.
12. Goldmann H (1946): A further note on the drainage of aqueous in man 112: 344.
13. Goldmann H (1948): A further note on the drainage of aqueous in man 116: 195.
14. Goldmann H (1949): A further note on the drainage of aqueous in man 117: 240.
15. Harms H & Dannheim R (1970): Epicritical consideration of 300 cases of trabeculotomy "ab externo". Trans Ophthalmol Soc UK 89: 491-499.
16. Harms H & Dannheim R (1970): Trabeculotomy - results and problems. Adv Ophthalmol 22: 121-131.
17. Harms H (1966): Glaukon-Operationen am Schlemm'schen Kanal. Sitzungsber, der 114 Versammlung des Vereins Rhein-Estf. Augenarzta.
18. Johnson DH and Johnson M: How does non-penetrating glaucoma surgery work?. In Mermoud A and Shaarawy T (Eds.) (2001): Non-penetrating glaucoma surgery. Martin Dunitz Ltd, United Kingdom. Chapter 4.
19. Kniestedt Ch, Kammann MTT, Stürmer J und Gloor BP (2000): Dysgenetische Kammerwinkelveränderungen bei Patienten mit Glaukom oder Verdacht auf Glaukom aufgetreten vor dem 40. Lebensjahr. Klin Monatsbl Augenheilkd 216: 377-387.
20. Koller T, Stürmer J, Remé Ch and Gloor B (1995): Risk factors for membrane formation in the chamber angle after failure of Argon laser trabeculoplasty. Ger J Ophthalmol 4 (Suppl 1): S11.
21. Kozlov VI & Kozlova TV (1996): Non-penetrating deep sclerectomy with collagen drainage implantation (ABSTRACT 9-02). 5th Congress and the Glaucoma Course of the European Glaucoma Society, June 1996, Paris. Abstract book: 120.
22. Kozlov VI et al (1990): Laser surgery for open-angle glaucoma in eyes with intraocular pressure elevation after nonpenetrating deep sclerectomy. IRTC Eye Microsurgery. RSFSR Ministry of Public Health, Moscow, 4: 62-66.
23. Kozlov VI et al (1990): Non-penetrating deep sclerectomy with collagen. IRTC Eye Microsurgery. RSFSR Ministry of Public Health, Moscow, 3: 44-46.
24. Kozlova TV et al (1996): Analysis of complications of non-penetrating deep sclerectomy with collagen implant (ABSTRACT 9-02.1). 5th Congress and the Glaucoma Course of the European Glaucoma Society, June 1996, Paris. Abstract book: 120.
25. Kozlova TV et al (2000): Non-penetrating deep sclerectomy: evolution of the method and prospects for development (review). Ophthalmosurgery 3: 39-53.
26. Krasnov MM (1964): Vestn Ophthalmol 77: 37-41.
27. Krasnov MM (1968): Externalization of Schlemm's canal (sinusotomy) in glaucoma. Brit J Ophthalmol 52: 157-161.

28. Krasnov MM (1972): Symposium: microsurgery of outflow channels - Sinusotomy: foundations, results, prospects. Trans Am Ophthalmol Otolaryngol 76: 368-374.
29. Malbran J (1957): Le glaucome pigmentarie, se relations avec le glaucome congénitial. Probl Act Ophtal, Vol 1, pp. 132-146, Karger, Basel, New York.
30. Mermoud A et al (1999): Nd:Yag goniopuncture after deep sclerectomy with collagen implant. Ophthalmic Surgery and Lasers 30: 120-125.
31. Mermoud A and Shaarawy T (Eds.) (2001): Non-penetrating glaucoma surgery. Martin Dunitz Ltd, United Kingdom.
32. Mizuno K, Asaoka M and Muroi S (1977): Cycloscopy and fluorescein cycloscopy of the ciliary process. Amer J Ophthalmol 84: 487-495.
33. Paufique L et al (1970): Technique et résultats de la trabeculotomie ab externo dans le traitement du glaucoma congénital. Bull et M de la Soc Franc d'Ophtalmol. Masson et Cie. Editeurs, Paris: 54-65.
34. Perkins ES (1955): Pressure in the canal of Schlemm. Brit J Ophthalmol 39: 215-219.
35. Sampaolesi R (1959): Neue Untersuchungen über das Pseudo-Kapselhäutchen-Glaukom (Glaucoma capsulare). Bericht über die 62. Zusammenkunft der Deutschen Ophtahmologischen Gesellschaft in Heidelberg 1959, pp: 178-183.
36. Sampaolesi R (1961): Semiología del Glaucoma. Tonometría, curvas tensionales diarias. Official Report presented at the 7th Meeting of the Argentine Society of Ophthalmology, Rosario 1961, Volume I, pp. 289-294.
37. Sampaolesi R & Reca R (1964): La courbe tensionnelle journalière dans le diagnostic précoce du glaucome. Etude statistique. Bull Soc Franc Ophtalmol 77: 252-261.
38. Sampaolesi R, Calixto N, Carvalho CA and Reca R (1968): Diurnal variation of intraocular pressure in healthy, suspected and glaucomatous eyes. Mod Probl Ophthalmol; 6: 1-23.
39. Sampaolesi R (1991): Glaucoma, 2nd edition, pp. 525-526. Editorial Médica Panamericana, Buenos Aires, 1991.
40. Sampaolesi R (1994): Jules Francoise Memorial Lecture. Congenital glaucoma. The importance of echometry in its diagnosis, treatment and functional outcome. Proceedings of the 15 SIDUO Congress, Cortina, Italy: 1-47.
41. Sampaolesi R et Sampaolesi JR (1998): Etude du nerf optique dans le glaucoma congénital par la tomographie confocale au laser. L'anneau d'Elschnig s'agrandit. Ophtalmologie; 12: 205-213.
42. Sampaolesi R. & Sampaolesi JR (1999): Confocal Tomography of the Retina and the Optic Nerve Head. City-Druck, Heidelberg.
43. Sears ML (1966): Pressure in the canal of Schlemm and its relation to tensite of resistance to outflow of aqueous humour in the eyes of Ethiopian green monkey. Invest Ophthalmol Vis Sci 5: 610-623.
44. Schuman JS et al (1999): Excimer laser effects on outflow pathway morphology. Invest Ophthalmol Vis Sci 40: 1676-1680.
45. Sourdille Ph et al (1999): Chirurgie non perforante du trabéculum avec implant d´acide hyaluronique réticulé. Pourquoi, comment, quels résultats? J Fr Ophtalmol 22: 794-797.
46. Stegmann R et al (1999): Viscocanalostomy for open-angle glaucoma in black African patients. J Cataract Refract Surg 25: 316-322.
47. Sugar HS (1961): Experimental trabeculotomy in glaucoma. Amer J Ophthalmol 54: 623-627.
48. Zarate JO (1999): Surface Light Microscopy (Abstract). XVIII Congreso Internacional de la Academia de Patología, Buenos Aires, September, 1999: 108.
49. Zimmerman ThJ et al (1984): Trabeculectomy vs. non penetrating trabeculectomy. A retrospective study of two procedures in phakic patients with glaucoma. Ophthalmic Surgery 15: 734-740.

6 Surgical Technique for the Molteno Seton

Anaika Concepcion, MD

The Molteno Single Plate Seton

This is the prototype drainage implant device and has had the longest and most extensive clinical experience since it was introduced by Molteno in 1969.[1]

Adequate surgical exposure is required, and is achieve by placing a traction suture. A 6-0 vicryl or silk suture is placed through the superficial cornea near the superior limbus, to function as the traction suture. Some surgeons, prefer to take the rectus muscle at each border of the selected quadrant is isolated, using a muscle hook; a 4-0 silk suture is positioned under each rectus muscle to act as a traction suture. The eyeball is then rotated using the traction sutures, with exposure of the sclera at the operation site.

A fornix-based conjunctival flap is raised over one quadrant of the globe, usually the superotemporal quadrant, to expose the sclera bed; if a previous surgery has already done, one of the inferior quadrants are chosen. The flap is slightly elevated to allow for blunt dissection between Tenon´s and epiesclera with blunt Westcott scissors. Is necessary to have a good surgical exposure to or beyond the equator of the eyeball, so radial relaxing incisions could be made on one or both sides of the conjunctival flap.

A caliper is set at 8 mm and a mark made 8-10 mm back from the cornea (posterior to the limbus) at each border of the quadrant, separating these marks 8 mm apart from each other. Two preplaced 5-0 Mersilene sutures are then placed through partial thickness of the sclera at each point marked off by the caliper **(Figure 1)**.

At this stage of the surgery, some surgeons choose to use antimetabolites as Mitomycin C; which is used in a titrated dosage followed by copious irrigation using balanced salt solution – but the use of mitomycin with setons is controversial. The plate of the Molteno implant is the tucked posteriorly into the sub-Tenon space along the scleral surface and secure with the preplaced 5-0 Mersilene sutures.

Next, the Molteno tube is cut, bevel up using a Vannas scissors. Before insertion of the tube into the anterior chamber, the limbal area (1.5 mm behind the limbus) is cauterized to prevent bleeding at the moment of insertion of the tube. A paracentesis is made at the limbus inferotemporally and a small amount of viscoelastic could be injected into the anterior chamber.

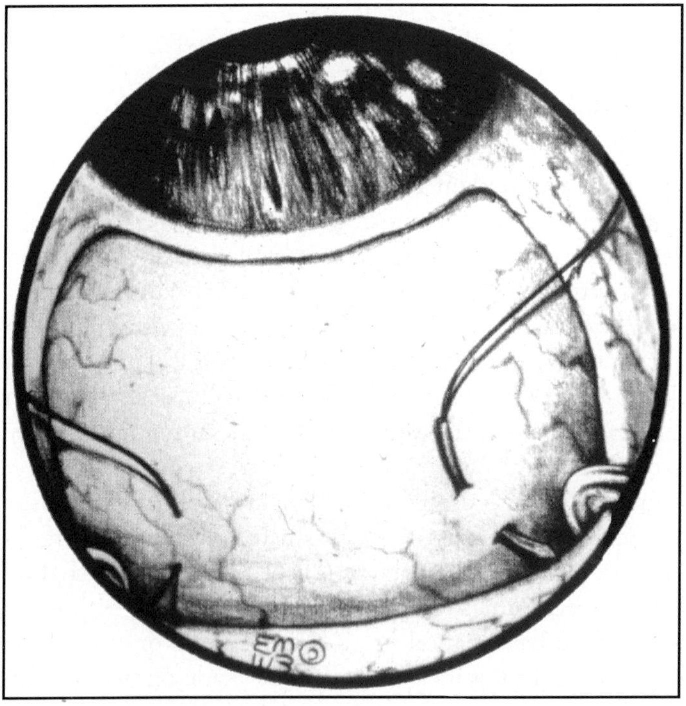

Figure 1: Fornix based conjunctival flap exposing quadrant of sclera. Pre-placed 5-0 Mersilene sutures 8mm behind limbus and 8mm apart.

Figure 1: A 4mm x 4mm lamellar scleral flap is raised. A 20-gauge needle makes a tract through the sclera into the anterior chamber, starting 1.5mm behind the limbus.

Using a 20-gauge needle, the anterior chamber is then entered starting at 1.5 mm behind the corneal limbus and directing the needle parallet to the iris surface **(Figure 2)**. The needle creates a water-tight seal, that follows the path of the Molteno tube. The needle is removed and the tube is thread through the track using a nontoothed or specially designed tube insertion forceps and positioned in the anterior chamber just anterior to the iris and well behind the cornea **(Figure 3)**. The tube should extend into the anterior chamber approximately half the distance from the corneal limbus to the pupil margin. If the tube is too long, it should be removed, shortened and replaced. The tube is secured to sclera with a mattress 10-0 nylon suture parallel to the tube, extending from a point just anterior to the base plate to a point just posterior to the limbus.

A 4x4 mm square of human processed pericardium (tutoplast from Biodynamics) is placed over to the tube and secured to the sclera at each corner with a 10-0 nylon suture. Also for this purpose could be used donor sclera, dura and fascia lata that are available commercially. An alternative procedure is to raise a 4x4 mm 1/3 thickness lamellar scleral flap and run the tube under this flap, securing it by suturing the flap back over the tube. This last method is illustrated in **Figure 3**.

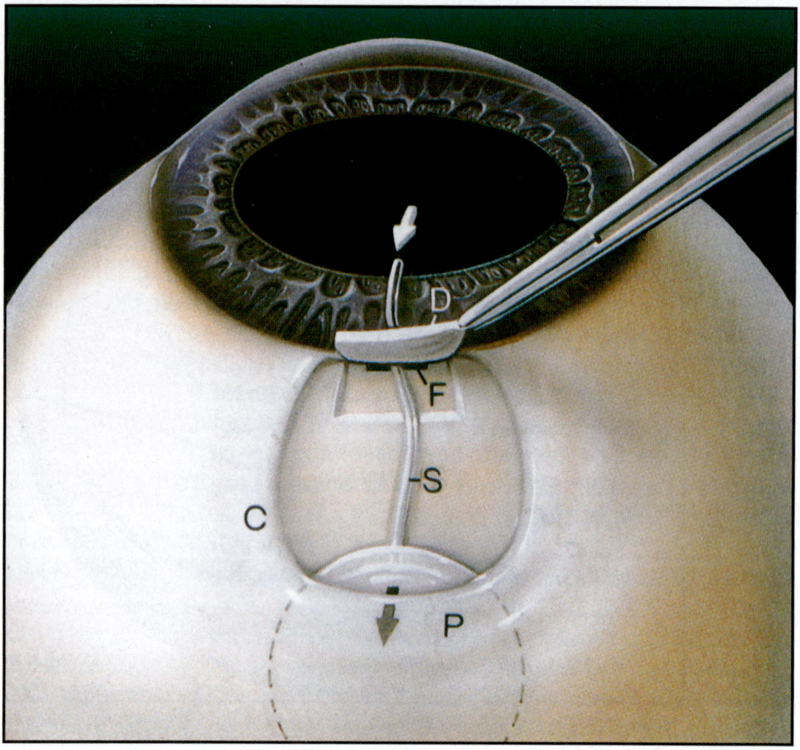

Figure 3: Seton Implantation Procedure. A fornix based conjunctival flap (C) is raised and the methylmethacrylate baseplate (P) of the Seton is pushed under the conjunctival flap posteriorly and sutured to the scleral surface. The implant has a biconcave shape with the inferior surface shaped to fit the sclera. A small 3mm square half thickness lamellar scleral flap (D) is raised just as in a trabeculectomy. An incision (F) is made into the anterior chamber under this scleral flap and the long silicone tube (S) of the Seton is placed into the anterior chamber (the end of the silicone tube can be seen in the anterior chamber near the tip of the white arrow). Next, the scleral flap (D) is sutured down around the tube (S) of the Seton. Finally, the conjunctiva is sutured back in place. Aqueous then drains from the anterior chamber (white arrow) down through the tube (S) to the baseplate (P) (black arrow), where a bleb forms. (Art from Jaypee Highlights Medical Publishers, Inc.)

The conjunctiva is then sutured back to its original position and could be secured using Vicryl sutures or continuous 10-0 nylon sutures to the limbus. During the procedure the anterior chamber may need to be deepened with balanced salt solution, or viscoelastic via the paracentesis, and the tube is checked for proper position in the anterior chamber.

Double-Plate Seton

The double plate Molteno, with twice surface area, is probably a better choice for most patients[2]; however, its two plates which are connected by a 10mm segment of silicone tubing require twice the amount of conjunctival dissection.

The second plate is sutured to the sclera in an adjacent quadrant following the same technique used for the first plate. After conjunctival dissection and opening of the posterior Tenon´s capsule the superior rectus muscle is isolated with a muscle hook. Attachments between the muscle and epiesclera are lysed with the aid of a second muscle hook. One of the Molteno implants is then passed under the superior rectus muscle; because of the difficulty of this maneuver and possible attendant trauma to the superior rectus muscle many surgeons prefer to place the interpolate tube over the rectus muscle. The remainder of the procedure continues the same as the technique used for the first plate.

Editorial Comment

The use of antimetabolites has significantly increased the success of filtration procedures in high risk glaucomatous eyes. As a matter of fact, a conventional trabeculectomy with antimetabolites generally seems to result in better intraocular pressure control levels than those obtained with an implant procedure without antimetabolites, unless the conjunctiva is very much affected by scarring.

Samuel Boyd, MD. Editor-in-Chief.

References

1. Molteno AC. New implant for drainage in glaucoma: clinical trial. Br J Ophthalmol 1969; 53:606).
2. Heuer D, Lloyd M, Abrams D, et al.: Which is better? One or two? A randomized clinical trial of single-plate versus double-plate Molteno implantation for glaucomas in aphakia and pseudophakia.Ophthalmology 1992; 99:1512

Bibliography

1. Shield´s Textbook of Glaucoma Fifth Edition. R. Rand Allinghan. Lippincott Williams. Wilkins. Chapter 41- Drainage Implants (pag 610 – 625)
2. Ophthalmic Surgery Principles and Practice. Third Edition. George L. Spaeth. Saunders. Chapter 30 Aqueous Shunts – Troy M Tanji MD. And Dale K. Heuer MD. (pags 297-308)

7 Surgical Technique for the Ahmed Glaucoma Valve (AGV)

Deepak Mishra, MD
B.P. Sinha, MS

Aim

To know the intraocular pressure (IOP) lowering efficacy and complication of the Ahmed Glaucoma Valve (AGV) in cases of refractive glaucoma.

Material and Methods

A prospective study of the Ahmed Glaucoma Valve (AGV) implant was done on 5 cases of refractory glaucoma (3 of NVG and 2 of aphakic glaucoma) at the Regional Institute of Ophthalmology (RIO) at Indira Gandhi Institute of Medical Sciences (IGIMS) and Institute of medical sciences (IMS), BHU in India between January 2009 to January 2010. Out of 5, 3 were male and one female who had positive family history of glaucoma. Patients belonged to age group of 40-50 years except one who was 24 year old.

A detailed preoperative assessment was done including applanation tonometry, gonioscopy, fundus examination and two reliable visual field by SITA 30-2 programme. The preoperative mean IOP was 40-50 mmHg and BCVA in the operated eye ≤ 6/60. The postoperative success rate was determined by target IOP between range of 10-20 without any antiglaucoma drug.

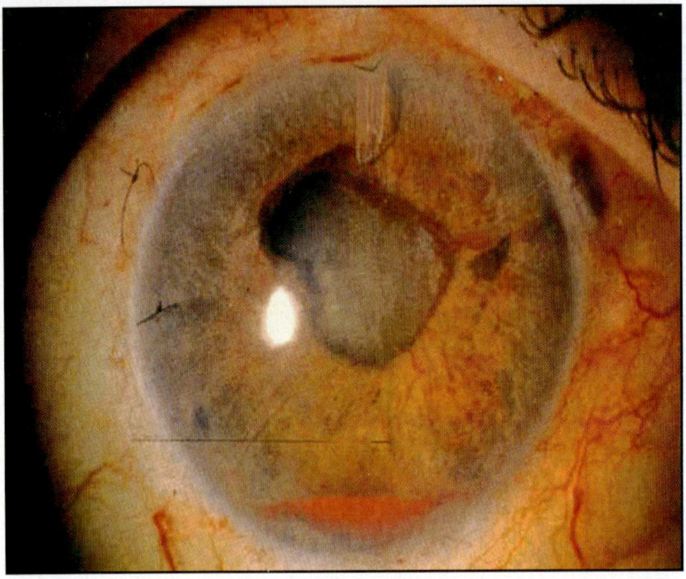

Figure 1: Shows valve tube in anterior chamber.

All the patients were subjected to AGV implantation in the superotemporal quadrant after reducing IOP with maximum medication. After giving local anaesthesia, adequate fornix based conjunctival flap was raised in super temporal quadrant to make a pocket large enough to slide the plate. The plate was inserted under the conjunctival flap and fixed 8-10 mm away from limbus. The tube was bevelled and trimmed then inserted into anterior chamber with help of 23 gauge needle and fixed to sclera by single suture. Scleral flap was sutured with 10-0 suture and conjunctival flap with 10-0 monofilament nylon suture. In all cases, surgeries were completed without any intraoperative complication **(Figure 1)** except some difficulty in inserting tube into the anterior chamber.

Postoperatively topical steroid was prescribed six times per day and subsequently tapered in the following weeks. Atropine eye drops thrice a day was given for a week and then stopped. A detailed postoperative examination include sterile IOP measurement by applanation tonometry, bleb morphology, tube position in anterior chamber, slit lamp examination and indirect ophthalmoscopy was done on day 1, day 7, week 1 month, 3 month and 6 month.

Table 1

S.No	Age/Sex	Diagnosis	Pre treatment IOP(mmHg)	DAY 1 IOP	Day 7 IOP	1 Month IOP	3 Month IOP	6 Month IOP
1	50/M	RE-Aphakic glaucoma LE-Adv IMSC	RE-42* LE-12	11	14	14	15	15
2	48/M	BE-NVG	RE-43 LE-45*	12	12	13	17	17
3	45/F	BE-Aphakic glaucoma	RE-47 LE-49*	10	13	17	15	16
4	24/M	RE-NVG+Old CR VO	RE-46* LE-16	9	12	12	10	13
5	40/F	BE-NVG+HR	RE-50 LE-48*	10	14	14	15	14

*- denote the operated eye LE- left eye , RE- right eye , BE- both eyes , IMSC- immature senile cataract, HR- hypertensive retinopathy , CRVO- central retinal vein occlusion

Results

The postoperative mean IOP on day 1, day 7 and 1month was 10.4, 13.4 and 14 mmHg respectively (showed in **Table 1**) without any anterior chamber reaction. At the end of 2 month, one patient reported the rise in IOP (28mmHg). Reason for rise in IOP was blockage of tube by iris tissue for which YAG laser ablation was done and his pressure again returned to 16 mmHg within 3 days. All cases were doing well with mean IOP reduction at 3 and 6 month were 14.3 and 15.1 mmHg respectively.

Discussion

Glaucoma drainage devices (GDD) are artificial drainage shunts which create alternative aqueous pathway between ant chamber & sub Tenon space. These are of 2 types, valved (Ahmad and Krupin valve devices) and non valved implants (Montero implants). Molteno implant *(Molteno AC; 1969)* is prototype and called Father of GDD. They are indicated in patients with elevated IOP or progressive disc damage or field loss despite of maximum tolerated medical therapy and failure of conventional filtration surgery/PRP.

The post operative complications associated with GDD are hypotony, elevated IOP, occlusion of tube, erosion and migration of tube and tube plate, endophthalmitis, diplopia and rarely RD. In our study we found low IOP on postoperative day 1 in all patients but only one patient had IOP<10mmHg. *Ayyala et al (1998)* and *Huang et al (1999)* also found hypotony in less than 10% of cases after AGV implant. Out of 5 cases, 1 have tube blockage by iris tissue and treated by Nd: YAG laser. Huang et al (1999) also observed tube obstruction in 11% cases in their study.

The overall efficacy of AGV is variable. *Coleman et al (1995)* and *Parihar et al (2008)* in their study showed success rate of 77 - 88.5% over 1 year of follow up. In our study success rate was 100%. It may be because of small sample size and short term (6 month) follow up.

Conclusion

AGV implantation is a potential mode of treatment in cases of refractive glaucoma. Studies on larger number of cases and longer follow up will show better usefulness of AGV implantation.

Editorial Comment

The idea behind implants is to enhance standard glaucoma surgery by positioning a device that will help keep the surgically-created drainage opening from healing and closing down. In special cases, the use of glaucoma drainage implant devices has improved the outcome in neovascular glaucoma and in glaucoma following uveitis, aphakia, and post-penetrating keratoplasty. To achieve this, many of the eyes require additional medical therapy either with one or more medications. It has also been demonstrated the safety and efficacy of surgery using drainage implants compared with trabeculectomy even for initial surgical management of primary open angle glaucoma.

Samuel Boyd, MD. Editor-in-Chief.

References

1. Ayyala RS, Zurakowski D, Smith JA et al. A clinical study of Ahmad glaucoma valve implant in advanced glaucoma. Ophthalmology 1998; 105:1968
2. Coleman AL, Hill R, Wilson MR et al. Initial clinical experience with Ahmad glaucoma valve. Am J Ophthalmol 1995; 120:23.
3. Huang MC, Netland PA, Coleman AL et al. Intermediate term clinical experience with Ahmad glaucoma valve. Am J Ophthalmol 1999; 127: 27.
4. Molteno AC. New implant for drainage in glaucoma: clinical trial.Br J Ophthalmol 1969; 53:606.
5. Parihar JKS, Vats DP, Mukherjee S et al. The efficacy of Ahmad glaucoma valve implants in cases of adult onset refractory glaucoma in Indian eyes: long term follow up. AIOS Proceedings 2008; 232-234.

8 Needling Procedure for Failed or Failing Filtering Blebs

Juan Roberto Sampaolesi, MD

The needling procedure in its various forms has evolved to salvage failed glaucoma filtering blebs caused by exuberant cicatrization including Tenon's cyst formation. Whether in a patient with recent or remote filtration surgery the goal is to avoid further intraoperative intervention and to reduce or eliminate medication. Although complications of in-office needling procedures parallel that of filtration surgery, they are an order of magnitude less in occurrence and needling is far more efficient than a repeat intraoperative procedure. The needling can be performed either in a minor procedure room or at the slit lamp if the surgeon is relatively ambidextrous. (*Editor's Note*: Some surgeons routinely use a minor procedure room or operating room because of the remote risk of post-procedure endophthalmitis.) For any skilled glaucoma surgeon the technique is easily mastered as long as careful planning and anatomical inspection are achieved. Additionally, a simple technique for salvaging impending failures of valved tube shunt surgery will be described.

Patient Selection

Patient selection is critical to the success of the procedure, especially if it will be performed at the slit lamp; since for the duration of the needling the patient must remain cooperative. With careful description of the procedure and preparation of the patient there is little difficulty maintaining concentration and positioning and with good technique there is virtually no discomfort.

The specific condition of the eye must also be well considered. Eyes that are overtly inflamed either from recent surgery or another cause should if at all possible be quieted first and needling delayed. Eyes with very thin avascular blebs or extremely scarred or thin conjunctiva should be avoided. Gonioscopy should be performed to examine the internal ostium in order to determine its size and patency. Special care must be taken in phakic eyes because of the added risk of cataract formation either from direct needle trauma or ensuing shallow or flat chamber.

Parameters for Success

The literature[1,2,3] identifies the parameters for a favorable outcome as 1) long-standing successful filtering blebs (the more remote the surgery the better); 2) fewer prior conjunctival incisions (reported in some but not all series); 3) those requiring only one needling (as opposed to multiple attempts); 4) an immediate post-needling pressure less than 10 mmHg;, and 5) possibly the use of adjunctive antimetabolite. Pre-needling intraocular pressure levels have been suggested in some but rejected in other series as a relevant factor.

The success of a needling procedure essentially depends on achieving three steps, namely: 1) lysing scar tissue or piercing Tenon's cyst; 2) ensuring an opened scleral flap; and 3) maintaining filtration into sub-Tenon's space.

Technique

After obtained consent and careful description the patient is given 2 successive drops of proparacaine and an antibiotic medication (alternatively povidone-iodine drops can be used). The periocular area is then carefully cleaned with betadine. A 1 cc syringe is used to draw-up a solution of 1% xylocaine with 1:100,000 of epinephrine and then a 30 gauge needle is placed on it. Sterile balanced-salt solution (BSS) is then placed in a 3 cc syringe with a 25 gauge 5/8 inch needle. Then the patient is readied for the procedure.

At the slit-lamp the the patient is comfortably seated and a lid-speculum is gently placed in the eye. Lubricant solution is immediately placed on the cornea to keep it moist during the procedure with the patient in the downgaze position. A sponge to rest the surgeon's ipsilateral elbow is used along with low magnification of the slit lamp.

The 1 cc syringe is then used to enter into the sub-Tenon's space and balloon-up, blanch, and further anesthetize the conjunctival tissue 7-9 mm posterior to the limbus. Only 0.1 - 0.2cc of solution is needed **(Figure 1)**. Then the 25 gauge needle with the BSS is used to enter through the first needle tract. The conjunctiva tissue is hydrodissected toward the edge of the scleral flap as needed. Higher magnification is helpful here in order to more easily visualize the advancing needle tip and the flap. If only conjunctival scarring is present without flap adherence

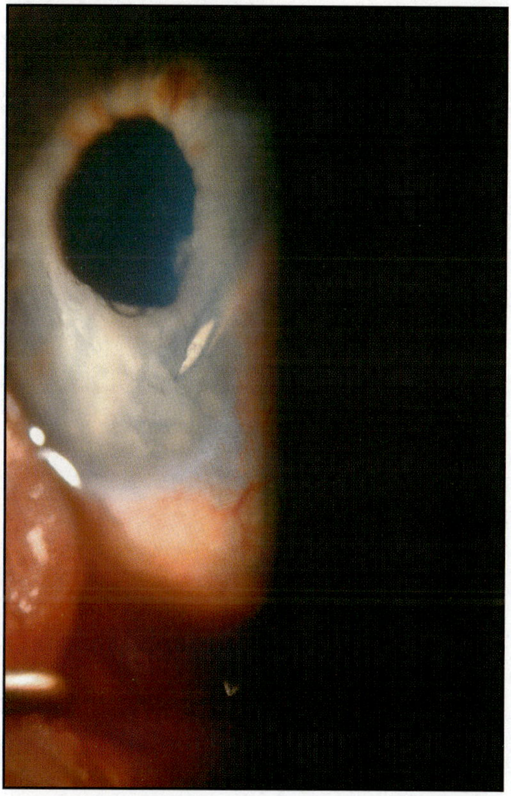

Figure 1: The patient is seated at the slit lamp. A 1cc syringe fitted with a 30-gauge needle filled with xylocaine 1% with 1:100,000 epinephrine enters the sub-Tenon's space 7-9mm posterior to the limbus. The solution is injected into the subconjunctival space, ballooning and blanching the overlying conjunctiva. Between 0.1 and 0.2cc of solution is used.

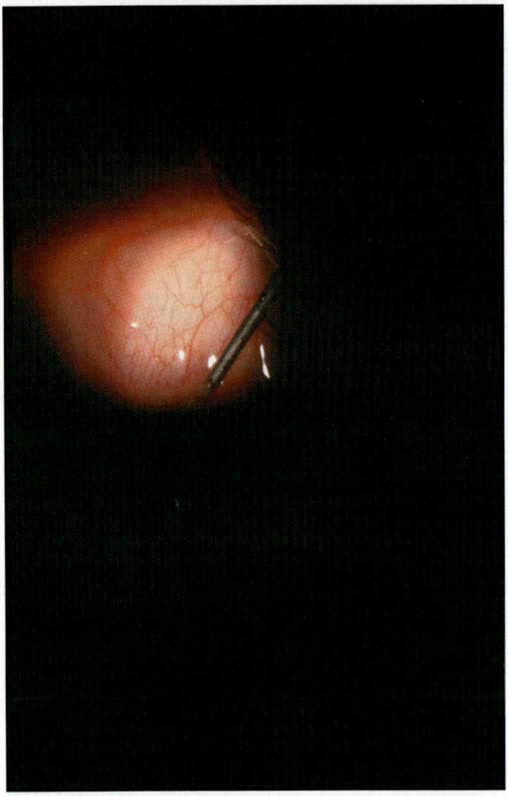

Figure 2: A 25-gauge needle on a 3cc syringe filled with BSS is introduced through the same needle track as the 30-gauge needle used in Figure 1. The 25-gauge needle is advanced toward the edge of the trabeculectomy scleral flap and, at the same time BSS is injected subconjunctivally to hydrodissect the conjunctiva as the needle advances towards the limbus.

then BSS will be noted to circulate in the anterior chamber and one may stop here **(Figure 2)**. If flap adherence is anticipated or observed then the patient is asked to slowly and with a very small movement to look up (now nearly straight ahead). If the needle tip is right at the ostium no resistance into the anterior chamber should be encountered with a small advancement of the needle tip. Now the needle tip can be seen in the anterior chamber **(Figure 3)**. Once this is achieved, the needle is withdrawn slightly back to the level of the edge of the flap and the needle is used to elevate it **(Figure 4)**. The beveled edge of the needle tip can be used to walk

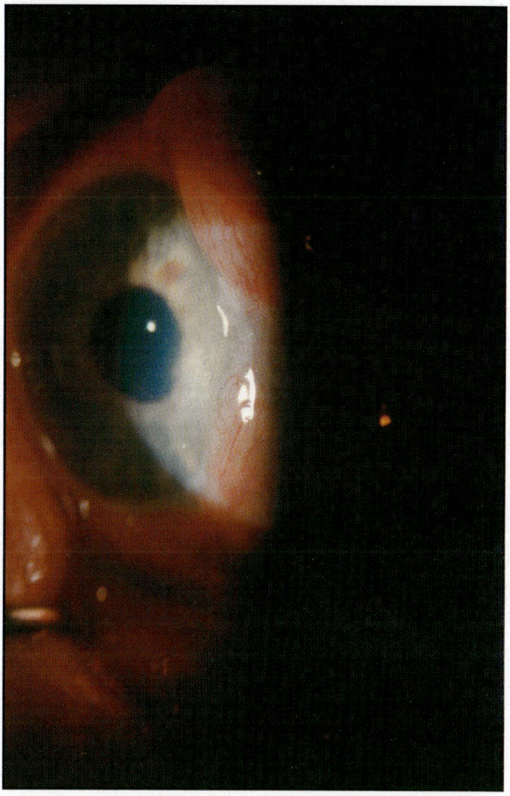

Figure 3: The patient is asked to look up slowly until the needle reaches the edge of the trabeculectomy flap. If the trabeculectomy flap is open there will be no resistance to the needle entering the anterior chamber, as shown in this illustration.

along the edge of the flap in order to ensure more complete lysis of adhesions. Next, the needle tip is placed above the plane of the flap and used to thoroughly hydrodissect the entire area surrounding the trabeculectomy site. The needle is then withdrawn.

The lid speculum is removed, antibiotic drops are instilled and the intraocular pressure is taken. If the pressure is above 10 mmHg the procedure is repeated immediately. If it is less than 10 mmHg the patient is instructed to use antibiotic drops and prednisolone acetate 1% every 1 -2 hours while awake and until seen

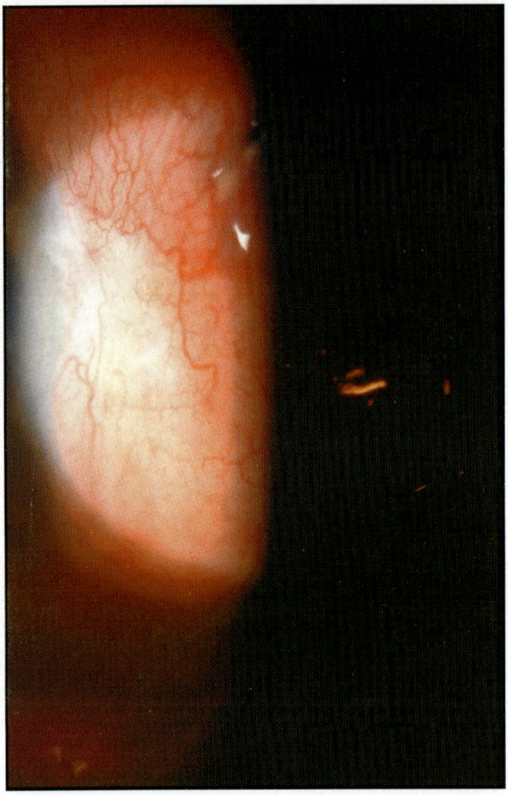

Figure 4: However, if the flap appears to be sealed, the needle tip is advance under the flap into the anterior chamber until the needle tip is visible in the AC. At this point, the needle is withdrawn to the level of the edge of the flap and is now used to elevate the flap.

the next day. A shield is worn at bedtime; however, no patch or shield is placed at the end of the procedure.

Before discharge the eye is reinspected at the slit lamp. Seidel testing usually will reveal a small leak at the needle entry site into the conjunctiva. Some advocate routine hand-held cautery of the leak at the needle entry site at the time of the procedure. However, within a 1 -2 days the leak usually closes without any significant flattening of the newly created bleb. If the leak persists beyond the first or second day then laser sealing of the needle tract is a good alternative. (Settings of 200-300 MW, 500 micron spot, 0.5 seconds with an argon laser is applied to the fluoroscein painted area identifying the leak.)

In the early post-needling period 5-fluorouracil can be injected as needed. An alternative technique has been advocated in one study: Mitomycin C (MMC) 0.1 ml of 0.4 mg/cc with 0.2 ml of Bupivacaine 15 - 20 minutes before the needling procedure. The success of the technique reported in this series; however, may not only be attributed to the adjunctive use of MMC, but also to the possible hypotensive effect of MMC, the multiple needling attempts for some the eyes in the series, or simply excellent technique. While the dose of MMC used in that series was carefully calculated to avoid any toxicity, one would advise caution in its use; and consider limiting its use to those cases with early bleb failure and attendant and exuberant inflammation.

Needling After Tube Shunt Surgery

In cases of tube shunt surgery with one-way valves (Ahmed, Krupin) that have impending failure a modified needling technique can be used to expand and maintain the bleb surrounding the plate. Here a 1 cc syringe with a 30 gauge needle is used. Hyaluronidase (Wydase) 0.2cc (30 Units), 0.1cc of xylocaine, 0.2cc of 5-Fluorouracil (10 mg), and 0.2cc of air are drawn up into the syringe. Neither a speculum nor the slit lamp are needed. Anesthetic and antibiotic medication are instilled. A pledget of anesthetic and 2.5% phenylepherine is placed over the intended injection site. The needle pierces the conjuctiva and the bleb 10 mm posterior to the limbus directly over the explant and is directed tangentially in a posterior direction. The 0.5 cc of cocktail plus the trailing 0.2 cc of air (used to tamponade the mixture from escaping through the tiny needle track) is then injected. Usually, the intraocular pressure can be observed to decrease immediately. The eye then is examined at the slit lamp. No anterior chamber reaction is observed. Mild temporary lid swelling and even ptosis may be observed. Antibiotic medication is applied four times per day for several days and the patient followed serially.

Conclusion

In summary, the needling procedure is an extremely efficient and effective method for salvaging a failed or failing filter. While its success rate may be slightly lower than an intra-operative procedure its reduced morbidity makes it an excellent addition to the glaucoma surgeon's armamentarium.

Editorial Comment

A failed bleb is to be differentiated from an encapsulated or cystic bleb where the conjunctiva forms a dome-shaped fibrotic wall with cavities that entrap aqueous humor. An encapsulated bleb can contain sufficient functional areas of filtration thus the IOP is not always elevated. Many patients who underwent filtrating eye surgery already showed insufficient response to IOP lowering topical medications, thus the importance of increasing the surgical success rate.

Samuel Boyd, MD. Editor-in-Chief.

References

1. Mardelli, P, Lederer, C, et. al. Slit-lamp Needle Revision of Failed Filtering Blebs Using Mitomycin C. Ophthalmology. 103: 1946- 55, 1996.
2. Greenfield, D., Miller, M. Suner, I, Palmberg, P., Needle Elevation of the Scleral Flap for failing Filtration Blebs After Trabeculectomy With Mitomycin C. Am. J. Ophthal. 122:195-204, 1996.
3. Metriyakool, K., Shin, D H., Kim, Y.Y., et. al. Risk Factors for Failure of 5-Fluorouracil Needling Revision of Failed or Failing Conjunctival Filtering Bleb. Invest Ophthal. 39: S5, 199.

9 Complications of Glaucoma Filtering Surgery

Marlene R. Moster, MD
Augusto Azuara-Blanco, MD, PhD

INTRAOPERATIVE COMPLICATIONS

Intraoperative Suprachoroidal Hemorrhage

Intraoperative suprachoroidal hemorrhage is a dramatic complication that can lead to loss of vision ("expulsive hemorrhage"). The incidence of suprachoroidal hemorrhage in glaucoma patients undergoing various types of intraocular surgery has been reported to be 0.73%. Risk factors include glaucoma, aphakia, previous vitrectomy, vitrectomy at the time of glaucoma surgery, buphthalmos, myopia, postoperative hypotony, arteriosclerosis, high blood pressure, tachycardia, and bleeding disorders. Nanophthalmos and Sturge-Weber syndrome have the highest risk for intraoperative suprachoroidal hemorrhage, which may occur in up to 30% of cases.

Intraoperative suprachoroidal hemorrhage can debut with sudden collapse of the anterior chamber, hardening of the globe, and prolapse of intraocular contents. The patient may experience pain breaking through the local anesthesia. A dark mass increasing in size can be observed through the pupil to evolve, but if the process is abrupt, the hemorrhage is more expulsive (i.e., ocular contents are expelled by the posterior pressure caused by the post-retinal hemorrhage) **(Figure 1)**.

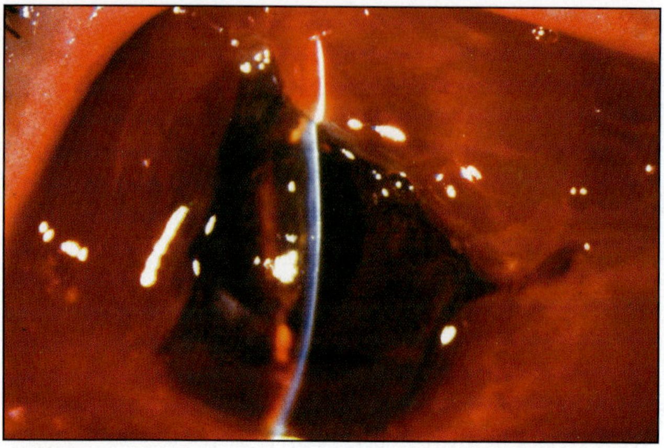

Figure 1: Large suprachoroidal hemorrhage with extension into the subconjunctival space following a trabeculectomy.

Treatment

Prompt and secure closure of the incision is the first goal of the treatment, with gentle reposition of prolapsed uvea. The surgeon's finger can be used to tamponade the incision site temporarily while sutures are placed and until the expansion of the hemorrhage is stopped. Intravenous mannitol 20% (1-1.5 gr / kg) is administered. Once the wound is closed, the anterior chamber is reformed with viscoelastics through a paracentesis. A conservative approach is recommended, although some authors propose immediate drainage of the hemorrhage through posterior sclerostomies (usually not possible because it rapidly clots). Prognosis for recovery of vision is uncertain but is better if the eye can be closed without loss of uvea and there is no intravitreal blood or retinal detachment.

Prevention

Several steps can be taken in "high risk" eyes: before surgery, correction of bleeding problems and discontinuation of inhibitors of platelet aggregation (e.g., acetylsalicylic acid) is recommended. Pre-operative intravenous mannitol at the time of surgery has been recommended but is controversial. Prophylactic sclerostomies can be considered in high-risk eyes. Use of viscoelastic or an anterior chamber maintainer and tight suturing of the scleral flap to prevent hypotony are recommended. In very high risk eyes such as nanophthalmos and Sturge-Weber syndrome, prophylactic sclerostomies can be considered before starting the filtering procedure.

Limbal vs. Fornix-based Conjunctival Flaps / Conjunctival Buttonholes

The type of conjunctival flap may influence the bleb morphology but has no influence on control of intraocular pressure. The theoretical advantages of the fornix-based conjunctival flap may include an improved exposure and access, a reduced risk of conjunctival button-hole formation, less trauma to Tenon's fascia, and the formation of a more posterior and diffuse bleb. However, with the fornix-based flap there is an increased risk of conjunctival wound leak in the early post-operative period if inadequately sutured **(Figure 2)**.

Conjunctival buttonholes and tears can lead to hypotony, flat anterior chamber and failure of bleb formation. Buttonholes and tears are more likely to occur in cases with extensive conjunctival scarring. The usual cause for conjunctival buttonholes is penetration of the tissue by the tip of a sharp instrument or forceps (toothed forceps should be avoided). To rule out a conjunctival buttonhole, the conjunctiva should be carefully examined at the end of the procedure by filling the anterior chamber through the paracentesis and raising the filtering bleb.

Figure 2: Fornix-based wound leak following trabeculectomy

If detected, a conjunctival buttonhole should be closed with a "purse string" knot done either internally or externally with a 10-0 nylon on a rounded-body ("taper-point") needle **(Figure 3)**. When the conjunctival buttonhole or tear occurs at the limbus, it can be sutured directly to the cornea, which may be de-epithelialized. A mattress suture or, if large, running or interrupted 10-0 nylon sutures can be used. When the buttonhole or tear occurs near the incised edge of a limbal-based conjunctival flap, it can be sutured to the wound.

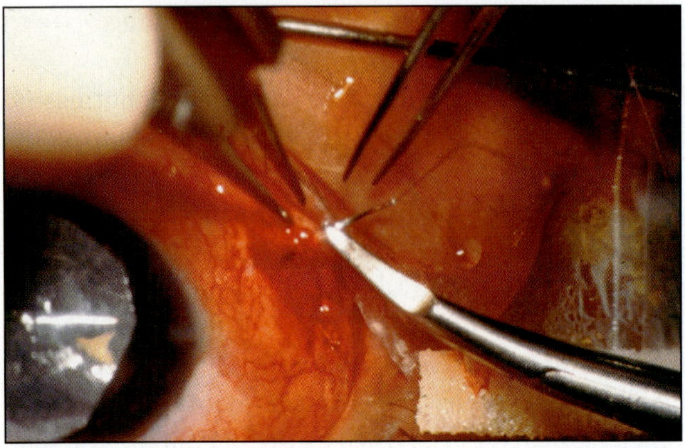

Figure 3: A buttonhole at the time of surgery requires closure with 10-0 nylon.

Scleral Flap Disinsertion

A thin scleral flap can be torn or amputated from its base, or become incompetent if handling has been excessive. If a sclerostomy has not yet been performed, a new scleral flap should be dissected in a different area. If a sclerostomy has been already done, re-approximation of the scleral flap can be attempted with 10-0 or 11-0 nylon sutures. If unsuccessful, a patch graft of Tenon's capsule or a flap of partial thickness sclera from the adjacent area is necessary to cover the sclerostomy. Alternatively, donor sclera, fascia lata or pericardium can be used **(Figure 4)**.

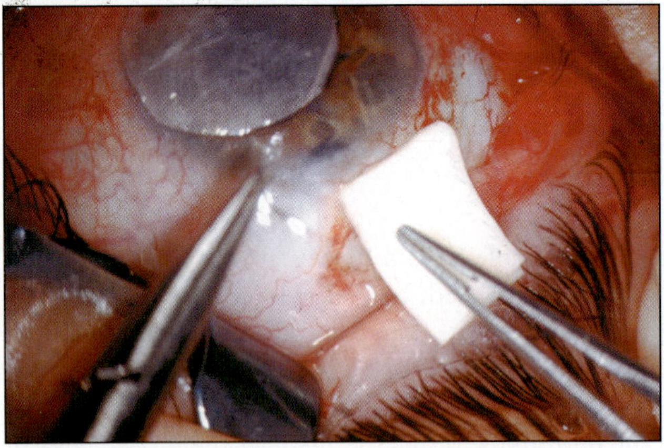

Figure 4: Tutoplast is used to cover a vigorous leak at the limbus.

Vitreous Loss

Vitreous loss is uncommon, although it may happen in patients with previous trauma, aphakia, buphthalmos, high myopia, a subluxated lens and severe pseudoexfoliation. Loss of vitreous can be associated with several complications and filtration failure. Vitreous should be removed from the surgical site and anterior chamber with a vitrectomy instrument.

Prevention

In aphakic eyes with vitreous filling the anterior chamber, an anterior vitrectomy can be planned as part of the primary procedure. In phakic or pseudophakic eyes with vitreous in the anterior chamber pars plana vitrectomy may be considered to adequately remove the vitreous from the posterior segment and to avoid lens/IOL subluxation and lens injury.

Intraoperative Bleeding and Hyphema

Bleeding commonly arises from the ciliary body or cut ends of the Schlemm's canal, although it might also arise from the corneoscleral incision or iris. **(Figures 5 - 6)** Minimal bleeding usually stops spontaneously. If a bleeding spot does not stop, the source of hemorrhage should be identified and coagulated, with care to avoid lens injury. During filtration surgery bleeding is decreased by performing the internal sclerostomy as far anterior as possible.

Treatment

If hyphema is recognized postoperatively, in the vast majority of cases no treatment is necessary and the blood will be absorbed within a brief period of time. Cycloplegics, corticosteroids, restriction of activity, and elevation of head of the bed 30 to 45 degrees (to prevent blood from obstructing a superior sclerostomy) are recommended. Increased IOP can occur, particularly if the filtering site is obstructed by a blood clot, and it should be treated if necessary with aqueous suppressants. Surgical evacuation is indicated depending on the level of IOP, size of hyphema, severity of optic nerve damage, likelihood of corneal blood staining, and presence of sickle trait or sickle cell anemia. Liquid blood can easily be removed with irrigation. If a clot has formed it can be removed by expression with viscoelastic or with a vitrectomy instrument set at low vacuum.

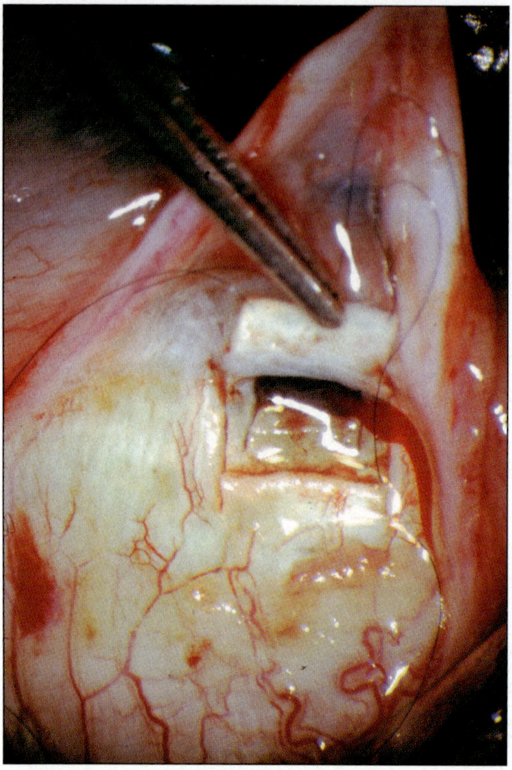

Figure 5: Following trabeculectomy, post-op hemorrhage usually occurs from the wound edge.

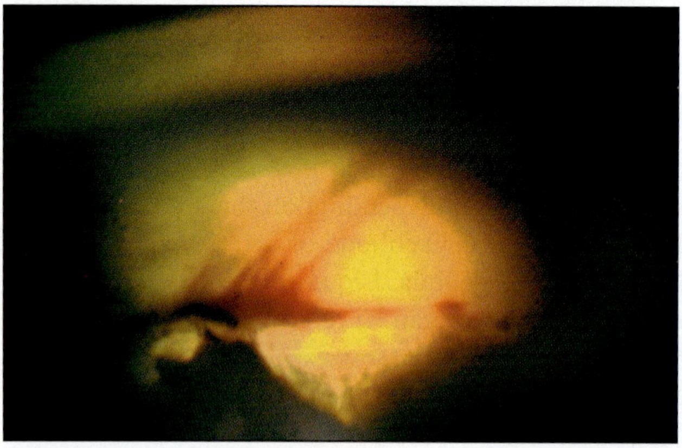

Figure 6: Gonioscopic view of bleeding from the wound edge.

Prevention

Discontinuation of inhibitors of platelet aggregation pre-operatively is recommended. It is important to avoid opening the fistula too posterior (to avoid the iris root and ciliary body, which may cause excessive bleeding).

POSTOPERATIVE COMPLICATIONS DURING THE EARLY POSTOPERATIVE PERIOD

Hypotony and Flat Anterior Chamber - Choroidal Effusion

Hypotony after glaucoma surgery can be due to excessive aqueous outflow (overfiltration, wound leak or cyclodialysis cleft) or to reduced aqueous production (ciliochoroidal detachment, cyclodialysis cleft, inflammation, and use of aqueous suppressants). These conditions can coexist. For example, low IOP due to overfiltration or wound leak can induce cilio-choroidal detachment and secondary decreased aqueous production. Severe choroidal effusions are likely in nanophthalmus and choroidal hemangiomas, even without marked hypotony.

The clinical findings are related to the mechanism responsible for ocular hypotony. At the slit-lamp examination the anterior chamber depth and certain bleb characteristics should be assessed. When there is a conjunctival buttonhole and leak, the bleb is usually flat; when the filtration is excessive and without leak there is an elevated bleb **(Figure 7)**.

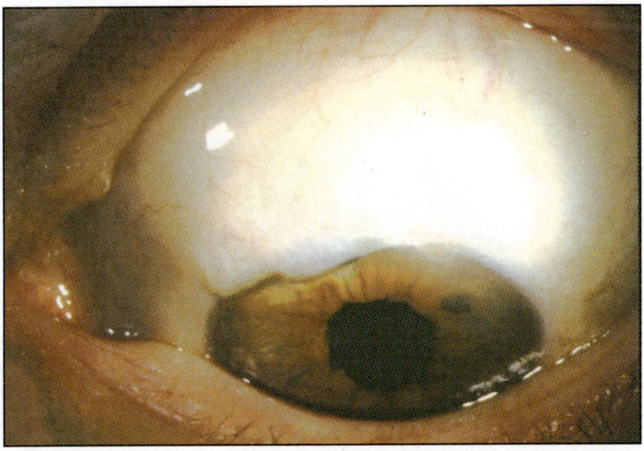

Figure 7: Large bleb with excessive filtration.

The severity of flat anterior chamber can be classified according to George L. Spaeth as grade I, when there is peripheral-iris apposition, grade II, **(Figure 8)** with pupillary border-corneal apposition, or grade III, with lens-corneal touch **(Figure 9)**. The central anterior chamber depth can be also described relative to the corneal thickness.

Hypotony in the early postoperative period can be associated with several complications. Fortunately, most cases are resolved with postoperative treatment allowing for preservation of the bleb function. Hypotony can induce cilio-choroidal detachment **(Figure 10)** (visible as mound-like elevations of the choroid, more commonly seen in the periphery), decreased aqueous production, gradual failure of the bleb, cataract, corneal edema or supra-choroidal hemorrhage. Corneal edema and Descemet's membrane folds are typically present.

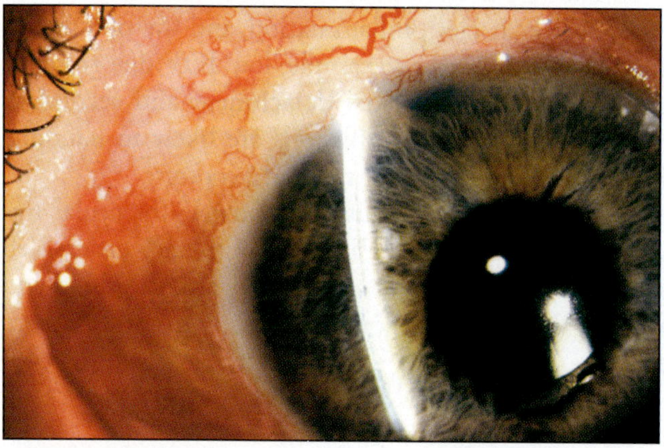

Figure 8: Grade II flat chamber with peripheral-iris apposition.

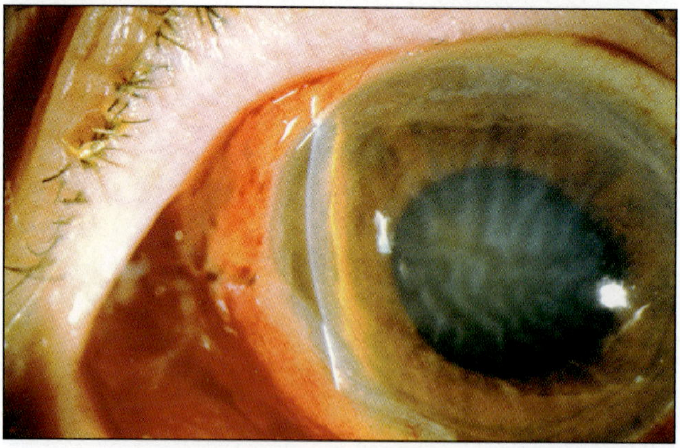

Figure 9: Grade III flat anterior chamber with lens-corneal touch.

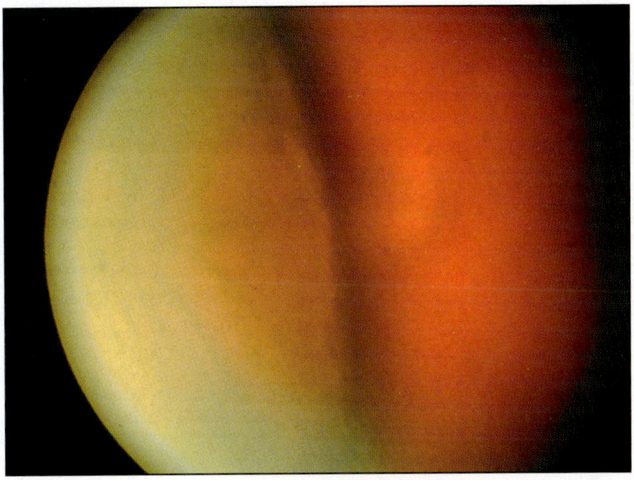

Figure 10: Large cilio-choroidal detachment with mound-like elevation of the choroid.

Treatment

The initial management of early postoperative hypotony with a formed or shallow anterior chamber is conservative. Topical steroids and cycloplegics are used. Restrictions in activity (bending, weight lifting) and avoidance of Valsalva-positive conditions are recommended, especially in patients at risk for suprachoroidal hemorrhage. If there is hyposecretion related to intraocular inflammation and/or ciliochoroidal detachment the initial treatment consists of intense corticosteroid therapy and long-acting cycloplegics that stabilize the blood-aqueous barrier. Tight closure of the scleral flap is recommended when there is a high risk of postoperative hypotony **(Figure 11)**.

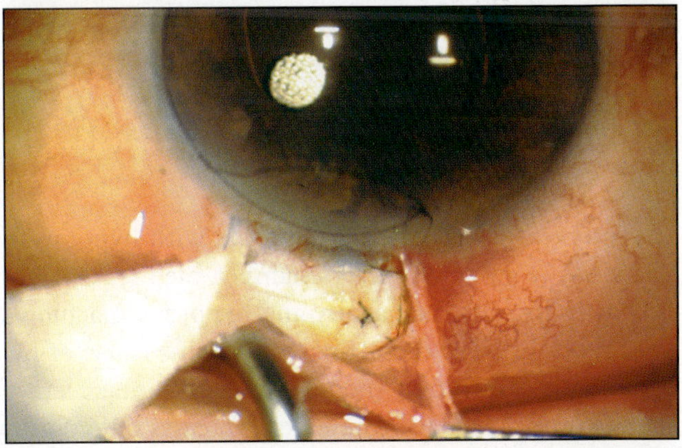

Figure 11: Tight closure of the scleral flap. This is recommended when there is a high risk of post-operative hypotony.

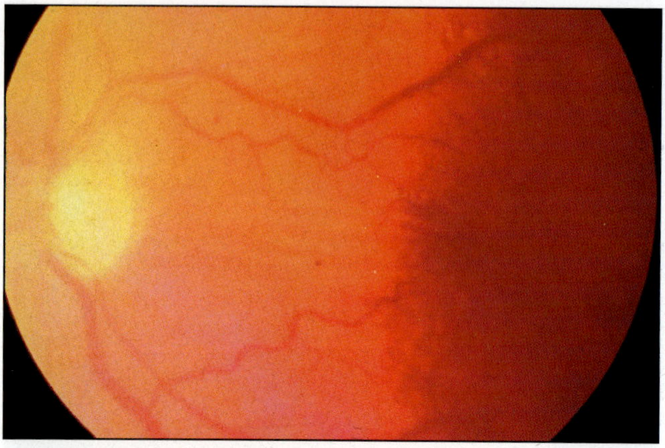

Figure 12: Hypotony with striae through the macula.

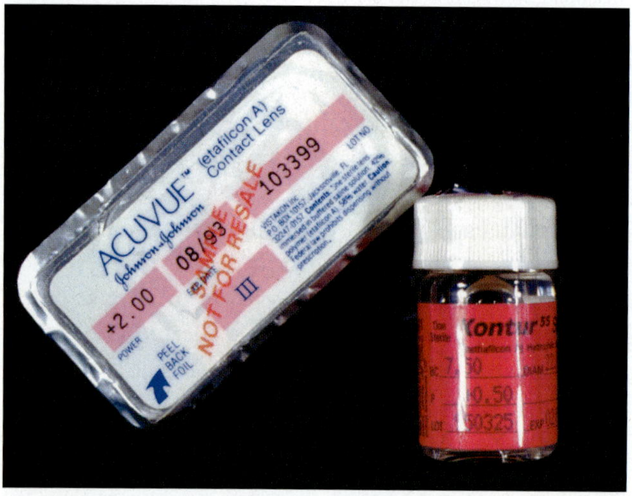

Figure 13: Large bandage lens (Kontourtm 22 mm in length).

Intervention is indicated in cases with hypotony associated with other complications (e.g., flat anterior chamber, bleb leak), and in eyes with persistent low IOP with loss of visual acuity and hypotony maculopathy **(Figure 12)**. Treatment should be aimed at correcting the specific cause of hypotony. The use of pressure patching, a 20-22 mm therapeutic soft contact lens **(Figure 13)** or a Simmons' shell **(Figure 14)** may be beneficial in cases of hypotony due to excessive filtration by tamponading the filtration site that allows gradual improvement in the anterior chamber depth.

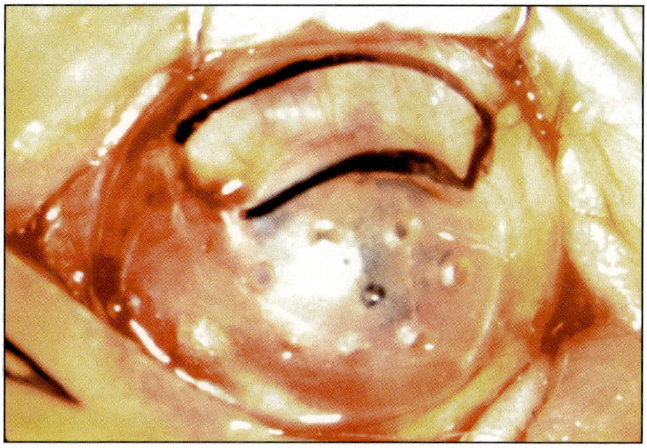

Figure 14: Simmons compression shell, placed over the filtering bleb.

The Simmons shell is usually effective but it may be uncomfortable, tonometry is not possible to monitor the IOP, decentration of the shell is frequent unless sutured to the conjunctiva, it requires close (daily) monitoring, and corneal complications (epithelial defects and abrasions) are common. A bandage contact lens is required. A therapeutic soft contact lens is preferable.

When there is lens-corneal touch (flat anterior chamber, grade III) immediate surgical intervention is necessary to prevent endothelial damage and cataract formation. Reformation of the anterior chamber with air, balanced salt solution or preferably by a viscoelastic can be done at the slit lamp or under the operating microscope through the paracentesis made intraoperatively. Viscoelastic material is best for maintaining, at least temporarily, the anterior chamber depth. If the flattening recurs, surgical intervention to address the cause of flat anterior chamber is required. When there are large and appositional choroidal effusions drainage of the fluid is also necessary.

Surgical drainage of choroidal effusions may be prudent in cases with persistent iridocorneal apposition and/or massive choroidal effusions with apposition of retinal surfaces within the macular area **(Figure 15)**. A sclerostomy is performed in one or occasionally in both inferior quadrants, and a tangential incision is performed in the sclera 4 mm posterior to the limbus. An infusion line can be connected to an anterior chamber maintainer through the paracentesis to maintain a deep anterior chamber while the choroidal effusion is evacuated. It is usually necessary for the surgeon to hold the sclerotomy open with forceps to facilitate drainage. A 1mm cyclodialisis spatula can be introduced into the suprachoroidal space if the choroidal effusion is thought to be loculated. Indirect ophthalmoscopic examination after drainage confirms flattening of the choroid. The sclerostomy site is closed with 7-0 Vycril, and the conjunctiva is closed watertight.

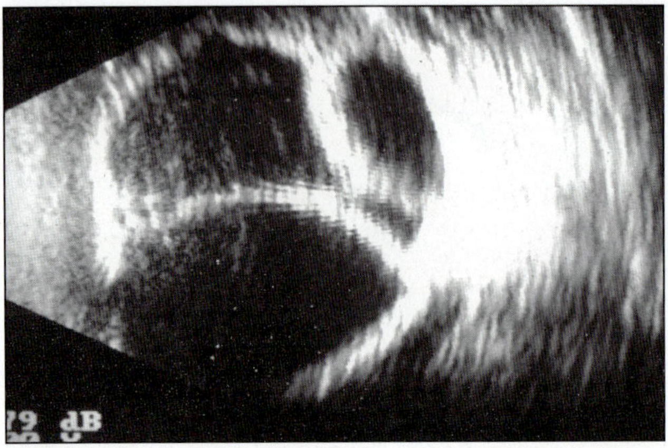

Figure 15: Large cilio-choroidal detachment with kissing choroidals and apposition of retinal surfaces.

In very high risk eyes such as nanophthalmos and Sturge-Weber syndrome, prophylactic sclerostomies can be considered before starting the filtering procedure, and left open.

Early Wound or Bleb Leak

Wound and bleb leaks are detected with the Seidel test. A wet fluorescein strip is applied to the inferior tarsal conjunctiva or, very gently, directly to the wound and bleb. Without applying pressure, the eye is examined under cobalt blue illumination. If there is a leak unstained aqueous humor will be seen flowing into the tear film **(Figure 16)**. If there is no spontaneous leakage pressure may be gently applied to the globe or to the bleb while the suspicious area is examined.

Small leaks around sutures often close without treatment. If there is a brisk leak, pressure patching or a large diameter (16-20 mm) soft therapeutic contact lens can be can be tried for 24 to 48 hours, or a 72-hour collagen (porcine) shield. Broad spectrum topical antibiotics should be administered to protect against infection, and close observation is mandatory. Fibrin tissue glue is a mixture of fibrinogen and thrombin which induces the formation of a clot that can seal bleb leaks. It is a non-irritating procedure that requires no patching. Autologous fibrin tissue glue (AFTG) is prepared from the patient's blood, therefore eliminating the risk for disease transmission. Cyanoacrylate glue (Histo-acryl, B.Brown Melsungen) **(Figure 17)** adheres to tissues and can effectively close an early wound bleb leak seen shortly after surgery. The glue must be applied to a dry conjunctival surface, and only a small amount of glue should be used. The use of a bandage contact lens can prevent the adhesive from being dislodged **(Figure 18)**. Suturing technique or wound leaks or buttonholes was described above.

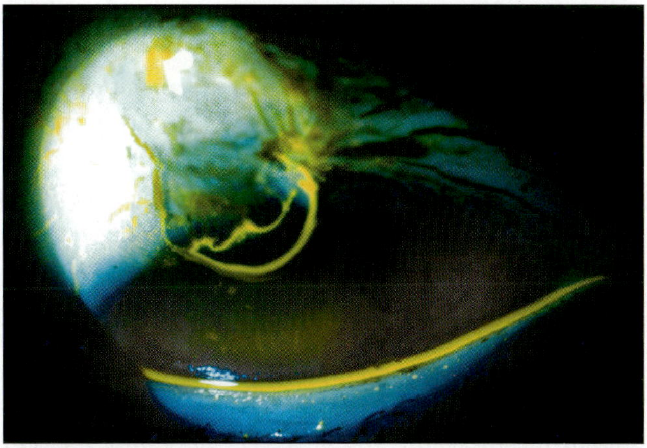

Figure 16: Seidel positive bleb, responsible for the IOP of 3 mm Hg.

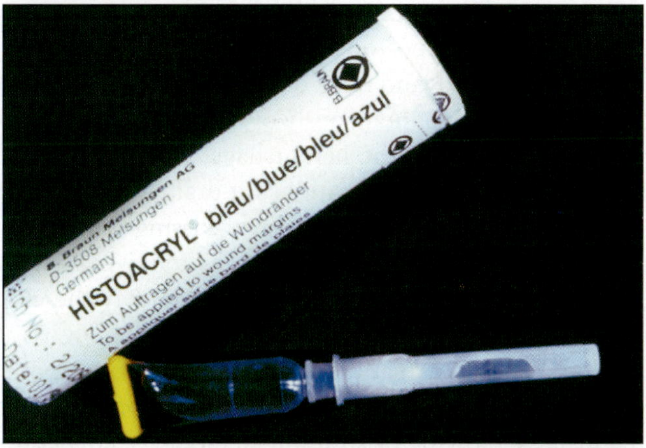

Figure 17: Cyanoacrylate glue which adheres to the tissue to effectively close an early wound bleb leak.

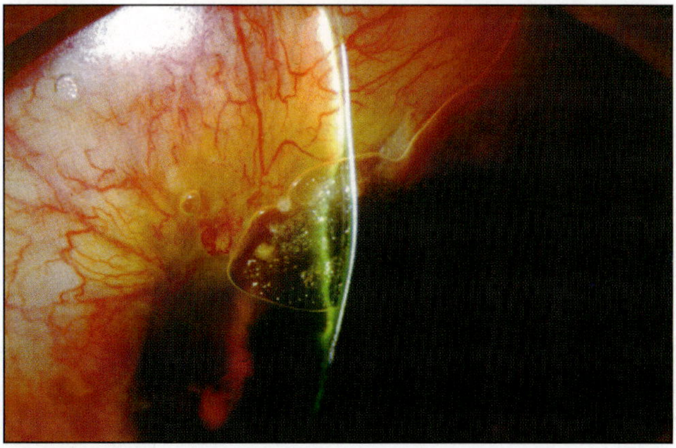

Figure 18: Use of a bandage contact lens can prevent the adhesive from becoming dislodged.

Suprachoroidal Hemorrhage

Postoperative suprachoroidal hemorrhage usually occurs within the first week after glaucoma surgery (most commonly during the first three days) and is usually associated with postoperative hypotony. Risk factors were described above (see Intraoperative suprachoroidal hemorrhage). Valsalva maneuvers may trigger the choroidal hemorrhage.

The development of a suprachoroidal hemorrhage is typically acute and associated with the sudden onset of severe pain and decrease in vision. Examination of the anterior segment frequently reveals a shallow anterior chamber and a normal or high intraocular pressure. On fundus exam a detached and dark choroid is noted. The choroidal elevations have a dark reddish brown color. Some cases present bleeding into the vitreous cavity and, uncommonly, retinal detachment. Ultrasonography can be used to diagnose suprachoroidal hemorrhage when fundus exam is not possible.

Treatment of postoperative suprachoroidal hemorrhage is directed toward control of the IOP and relief of pain. The majority of small to medium-sized hemorrhages resolve spontaneously over subsequent weeks. Bleeding into the vitreous cavity at the time of the hemorrhage, and retinal detachment greatly worsen the visual prognosis. The indications for drainage include intolerable pain, a persistent flat anterior chamber, and massive "kissing" choroidal detachments (Figure 15). A waiting period of about two weeks following a suprachoroidal hemorrhage is advised for the fibrinolytic response to liquefy the clot, which may be confirmed by B-scan ultrasound.

Prevention. The patient is urged to restrict activities (bending, weight lifting) and to avoid Valsalva-positive conditions (constipation, vigorous coughing, sneezing or nose-blowing or straining at stool – *Editor*) during the early postoperative period. Postoperative hypotony should be avoided in high risk eyes.

Aqueous Misdirection

Aqueous misdirection or "malignant glaucoma" or "ciliary block glaucoma" is characterized by a shallowing or flattening of the anterior chamber **(Figure 19)** even in the presence of a patent iridectomy and absence of chorioretinal pathology (such as suprachoroidal hemorrhage), commonly with an accompanying rise in intraocular pressure (IOP). The chance of developing malignant glaucoma is greatest in phakic hyperopic (small) eyes with angle closure glaucoma. It occurs in 2% to 4% of patients operated on for angle closure glaucoma.

In this condition aqueous is diverted posteriorly towards the vitreous cavity and trapped in the vitreous cavity, increasing the vitreous volume and shallowing the anterior chamber. Small choroidal effusions and shallow anterior chamber sometimes occur before the episode of aqueous misdirection. In some cases pupillary block occurs first and is followed by aqueous misdirection **(Figure 20)**.

Aqueous misdirection usually occurs in the early postoperative period after filtration surgery **(Figure 21)**. The anterior chamber is shallow and the intraocular pressure is commonly high. However, with a functioning filtration bleb the intraocular pressure may be within normal limits. If the adequacy of the surgical iridectomy is in doubt and pupillary block is possible, a laser iridotomy should be performed.

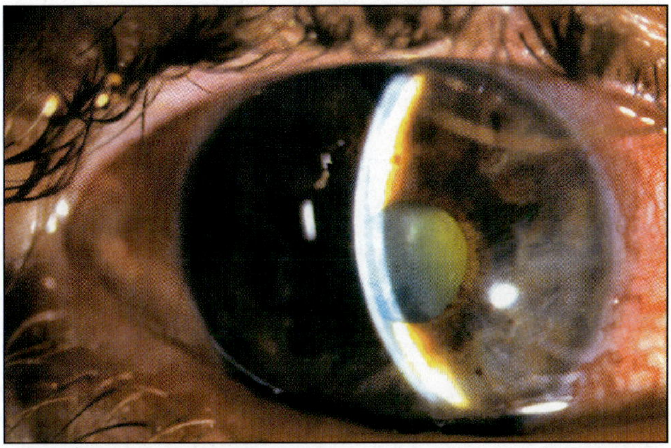

Figure 19: Aqueous misdirection in a phakic hyperopic eye.

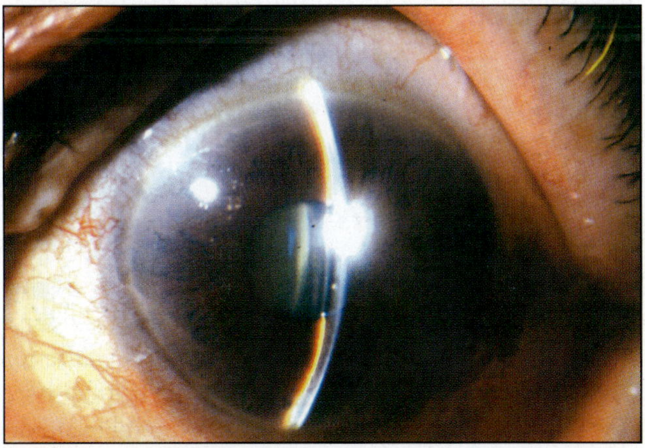

Figure 20: Pupillary block with an extremely shallow anterior chamber and elevated IOP. No iridectomy is present.

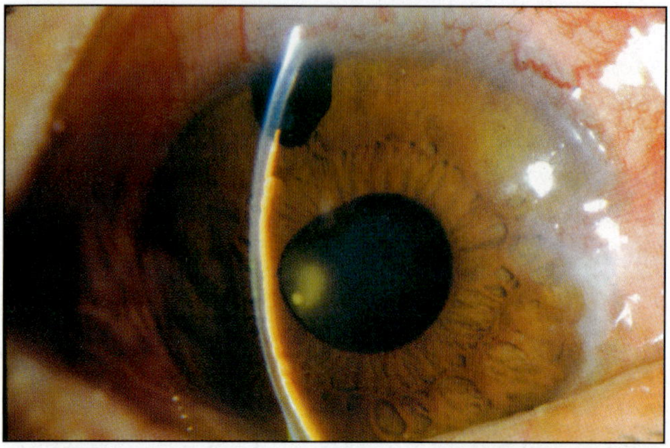

Figure 21: Malignant glaucoma or aqueous misdirection following a trabeculectomy with a Grade II flat anterior chamber.

Medical treatment, laser and vitreous surgery have all been useful options to treat aqueous misdirection. This condition is initially managed with mydriatic-cycloplegic drops, aqueous suppressants and hyperosmotics. Topical 1% atropine or 1% cyclopentolate four times daily and 2.5% phenylephrine four times daily are used. These agents hopefully will result in a posterior movement of the lens-iris diaphragm. In cases of aphakic aqueous misdirection, mydriatic-cycloplegic drops are of little benefit. However, it is reasonable to use them for their effect on relaxation of the ciliary body muscle. Systemic carbonic anhydrase inhibitors and topical beta-adrenergic blocking agents in full doses are important. Osmotics (isosorbide, glycerin, or intravenous mannitol) can be also very helpful to decrease the fluid content of the vitreous cavity, and can be repeated after 12 hours with cautious control of electrolytes, hydration, and possible systemic complications. If it is well tolerated and there are no contraindications, the medical treatment is tried for 2-4 days. If the condition is relieved (i.e., the anterior chamber has deepened), the hyperosmostic agents are discontinued first, and the aqueous suppressants are reduced or even stopped over several days. Phenylephrine drops can be stopped, but the cycloplegic drops can be continued for months. Medical treatment relieves about 50% of cases of aqueous misdirection.

If medical therapy is unsuccessful and the ocular media are clear, a Nd:YAG laser capsulotomy and hyaloidotomy is used to disrupt the anterior vitreous face in pseudophakic and aphakic cases. The initial laser energy is between 2 and 4 millijoules. The focus is placed posterior to the anterior hyaloid. After a successful Nd:YAG hyaloidotomy a slight deepening is usually seen, which increases over the next hours. In pseudophakic eyes, a peripheral hyaloidotomy is more efficient than a central hyaloidotomy because the lens capsule and intraocular lens can prevent communication between the vitreous cavity and the anterior chamber. In phakic eyes, Nd:YAG hyaloidotomy can be tried through the peripheral iridectomy, focusing behind the zonules but in front of the ciliary body. However, a clear view and sharp focusing may not be possible, and there is a risk of lens or zonular injury.

Pars plana vitrectomy can be considered when other therapies fail. A standard 3-port pars plana (23G or 25G) vitrectomy, removing the anterior vitreous and part of the anterior hyaloid, is done. In phakic patients, the lens can sometimes be spared, but the probability of recurrence is higher. Pars plana tube-shunt insertion with vitrectomy has been recommended to treat patients with aqueous misdirection, especially in cases with angle closure glaucoma. The implantation of the tube shunt through pars plana can help prevent recurrence of this condition and can help in long-term control of IOP. (A large patent peripheral iridectomy or multiple peripheral iridectomies must be in place).

Alternatively, phakic eyes that do not respond to medical therapy and pars plana vitrectomy can be successfully treated with phacoemulsification of the lens, posterior capsulectomy and anterior vitrectomy. In pseudophakic eyes a vitreous cutter can be introduced through the anterior chamber through a paracentesis, associated with an anterior chamber maintainer. The vitreous cutter is used to enlarge the peripheral iridectomy and then is directed posteriorly to do a localized zonulo-hyaloido-vitrectomy (Lois' technique).

Prevention: In high risk eyes undergoing filtration surgery the decompression and shallowing of the anterior chamber should be minimized. The use of viscoelastic and a large peripheral iridectomy can be helpful. Because aqueous misdirection can occur during filtration surgery, eyes with intraoperative shallow anterior chamber and high IOP should be treated promptly with intraoperative mannitol and cycloplegics. Tight suturing of the scleral flap is also needed. Aqueous suppressants should be also considered.

Postoperative overfiltration should be avoided with a thick scleral flap sutured tighter and with more sutures than usual **(Figure 11)**. Postoperatively, judicious suture lysis or cutting/pulling releasable sutures and slow tapering of cycloplegics are recommended. A postoperative shallow anterior chamber due to overfiltration should be vigorously treated.

Pupillary Block

Pupillary block can be caused by adhesions between the iris and lens, pseudophakos, or vitreous. The inability of aqueous humor to pass from the posterior to the anterior chamber results in the forward movement of the peripheral iris and closure of the drainage angle. Pupillary block typically occurs as a flat or shallow anterior chamber with normal or elevated pressure. It may be difficult to distinguish from malignant glaucoma (or it may be considered as part of the clinical spectrum of malignant glaucoma).

Although a peripheral iridectomy is intended at the time of filtration surgery, in a few cases only the stroma of the iris is removed and the posterior pigment epithelium is left intact. In these cases blockage may develop. In other cases the iris may become incarcerated in the wound, or the iridectomy may be obstructed by intraocular tissue, such as Descemet's membrane, anterior hyaloid surface, vitreous (in aphakic eyes), or ciliary processes. If the IOP is high and the anterior chamber is flat after a patent peripheral iridectomy has been confirmed, malignant glaucoma should be considered.

Therapy with cycloplegic-mydriatics may resolve pupillary block but a Nd:YAG peripheral iridotomy should be done. The anterior chamber will readily deepen after iridotomy is performed, although in presence of localized compartments of blockage multiple iridotomies are necessary. This deepening is usually associated with the sudden escape of aqueous humor through the iridectomy and confirms the diagnosis of pupillary block. If laser iridotomy cannot be completed a surgical iridectomy should be done.

Early Failure of Filtering Bleb

Early failure of filtering blebs is characterized by a high IOP, deep anterior chamber and low filtering bleb **(Figure 22)**. A tight scleral flap and episcleral fibrosis are the most common causes of early bleb failure. Internal obstruction of the fistula by blood clot, vitreous, iris, or incompletely excised Descemet's membrane is also possible.

Failing blebs should be recognized promptly because if obstruction is not relieved permanent adhesions between conjunctiva and episclera can lead to failure of the bleb. The most important period is between the first and fourth weeks, when the inflammatory response is maximal.

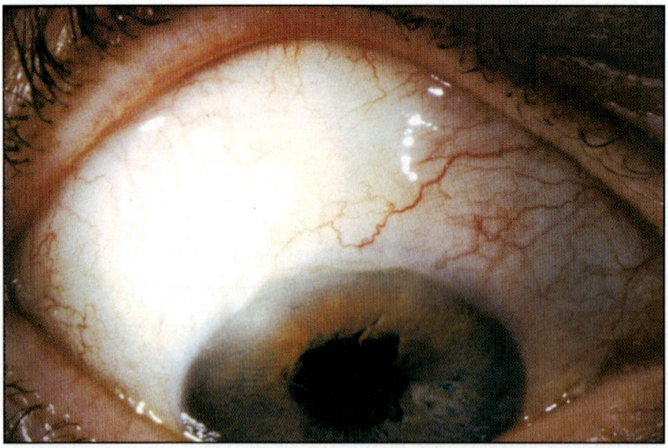

Figure 22: Failed bleb shortly after fornix-based trabeculectomy.

Complications associated with the use of postoperative 5-FU include corneal and conjunctival epithelial toxicity, **(Figure 23)** corneal ulcers, **(Figure 24)** conjunctival wound leaks, subconjunctival hemorrhage, or inadvertent intraocular spread of 5-FU. The frequency of complications is reduced with lower dosages of 15 - 50 mg administered in 3 -10 injections, each of 5 mg, according to individual response. Mitomycin-C is approximately 100 times more potent than 5-FU. Postoperative complications associated with overfiltration, hypotony maculopathy, bleb leak, and bleb-related ocular infections are more likely to occur when mitomycin-C is used.

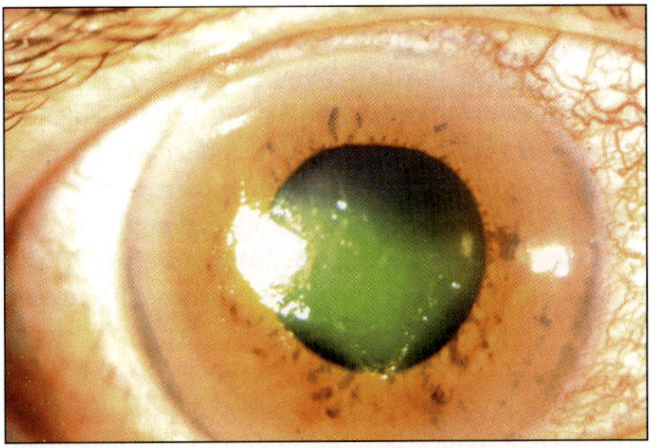

Figure 23: Confluent SPK following 5-FU injection.

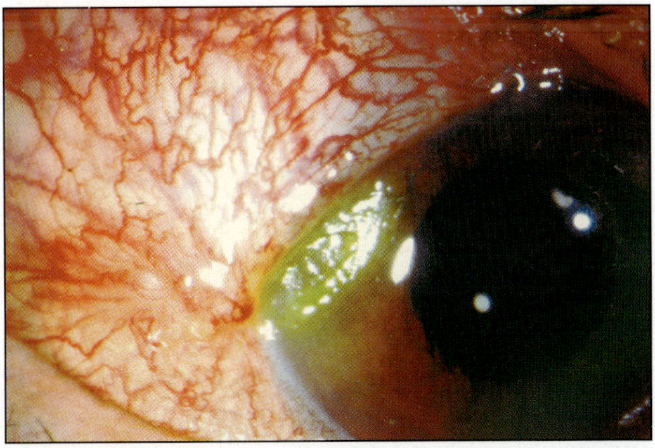

Figure 24: Dellen following trabeculectomy with 5-FU.

During the first few days, digital ocular massage and focal distortion of the scleral flap can be used to temporarily improve the function and elevate the filtering bleb. Digital ocular compression (DOC) can be applied to the inferior sclera or cornea through the inferior eye-lid, or to the sclera posterior to the scleral flap through the superior eye-lid. Focal compression is applied with a moistened cotton tip or blunt instrument at the edge of the scleral flap.

Laser suture lysis can enhance the filtration during the early postoperative period. The timing of suture release is critical. Suture lysis is effective within the first two weeks after surgery without antimetabolites; later, fibrosis of the scleral flap may negate any beneficial effect of this procedure. If antimetabolites have been used at the time of surgery suture lysis can be effective several weeks after surgery. Specially designed lenses such as Hoskins, Ritch or Mandelkorn lens, the central button edge of the Zeiss and Sussman lenses, the Goldmann lens, glass rods or glass pipettes can be used. After the suture is cut, if the bleb elevates, **(Figure 25)** no additional sutures need to be cut. If the bleb and IOP are unchanged, ocular massage or focal pressure can be applied and, if there is no change in the bleb, another suture should be cut. When there is subconjunctival hemorrhage a diode laser should be used because their wavelengths are least absorbed by blood.

Releasable sutures **(Figure 26)** are as effective as laser suture lysis. The externalized sutures are easily removed and are effective in cases of hemorrhagic conjunctiva or thickened Tenon's tissue (that would make difficult suture lysis). The disadvantages of releasable sutures include the need for additional intraoperative manipulation and possibly increased risk of ocular infection. Several techniques have been described (see Section on Trabeculectomy for description of releasable sutures).

If these procedures fail then the bleb can be needled **(Table 1)**.

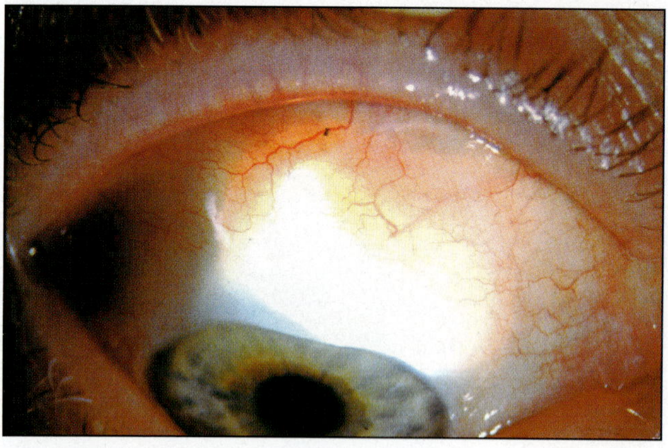

Figure 25: Bleb elevation after laser suture lysis.

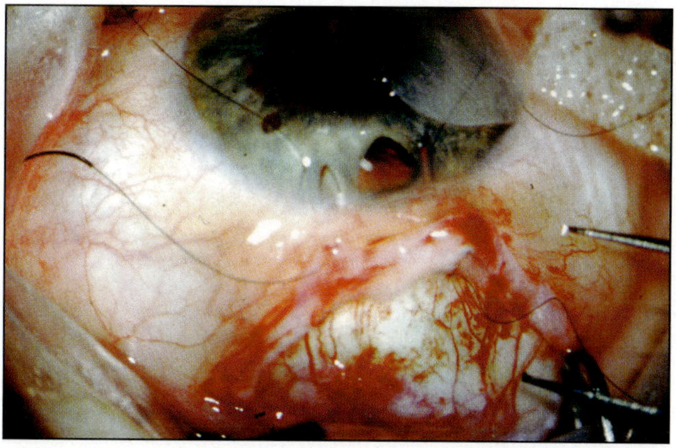

Figure 26: Releasable sutures tied into clear cornea at the time of trabeculectomy surgery.

Table 1
Needling of Filtering Bleb

1. The procedure can be done at the slit lamp or in the operating room.
2. Topical anesthesia is used. A cotton pledget can be soaked in the anesthetic and applied to the area of injection. Topical phenylephrine 2.5% is used to vasoconstric the conjunctival vessels (optional).
3. Povidone-iodine 5% solution is applied to the conjunctiva, eyelid margins, eyelashes and eyelids.
4. A lid speculum can be used (optional).
5. On a tuberculin syringe a 30- or 27-gauge needle penetrates the conjunctiva, 5 to 10 mm from the scleral fistula (through conjunctiva not treated with an antifibrosis regimen).
6. Balanced salt solution or lidocaine can be injected to raise the conjunctiva (optional).
7. The needle is then advanced into the bleb cavity and beneath the scleral flap. A sweeping motion or to and fro movements is done with the edge or the tip of the needle, respectively.
8. "Aggressive alternative": the needle can be advanced through the internal ostium (optional) until the needle is visualized in the anterior chamber (this procedure should be done with extreme caution in phakic eyes).
9. Then end point is elevation of the bleb rises IOP reduction.
10. A Seidel test should be done to evaluate wound leaks through the conjunctival entry point, which can be cauterized.
11. Postoperatively, topical antibiotics and steroids are used, with or without additional injections of 5-FU.

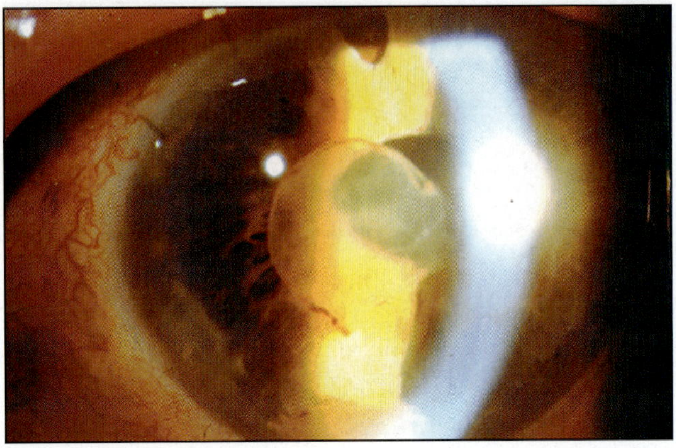

Figure 27: Fibrinous clot in the anterior chamber following glaucoma filtering surgery.

When the cause of filtration failure is a blood clot or fibrinous clot **(Figure 27)** occluding the sclerostomy tissue plasminogen activator (tPA) can be helpful. Recombinant tPA is a protease with clot-specific fibrinolytic activity. It can be injected into the anterior chamber or subconjunctivally and the dosage is 7-10 micrograms in 0.1 ml. It works rapidly so that within 3 hours the effect is usually apparent. Hyphema is the most frequent complication, and tPA should be consider only if there is no active or recent bleeding. Alternatively, the blood clot can be dispersed by exposing it to Nd:YAG laser with settings at 1.5 to 2.0 mJ power via a gonioscopic lens.

Encapsulated Blebs

Encapsulated blebs, also called Tenon's cysts, are localized, elevated and tense filtering blebs, with vascular engorgement of the overlying conjunctiva and a thick connective tissue **(Figure 28)**. This type of bleb commonly appears within 2 to 6 weeks following surgery. Encapsulation of the filtering bleb is associated with a rise of IOP after an initial period of pressure control following glaucoma surgery. They can interfere with upper lid movement and tear film distribution leading to corneal complications such us dellen (Figure 24) and astigmatism. Often it is seen through the eyelid simulating a lid mass.

The frequency of bleb encapsulation after trabeculectomies without antimetabolites ranges from 8.3% to 28% **(Figure 29)**. Predisposing factors may include male gender, glove powder, and prior treatment with sympathomimetics, argon laser trabeculoplasty, and surgery involving the conjunctiva. The long-term prognosis for IOP control in eyes that develop encapsulated bleb is relatively good.

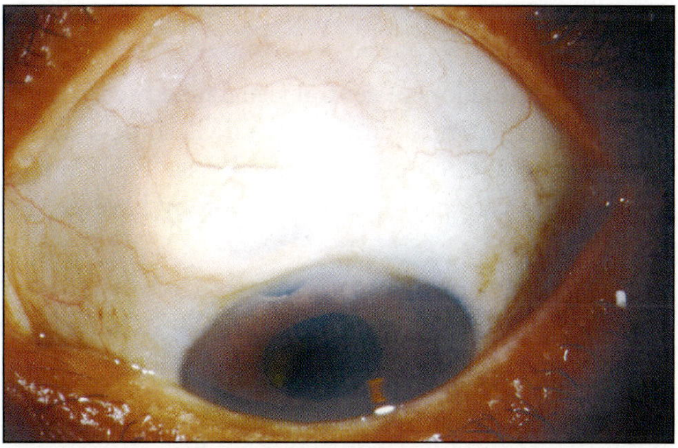

Figure 28: Encapsulated Tenon's cyst with high tight bleb, IOP 36 mm Hg.

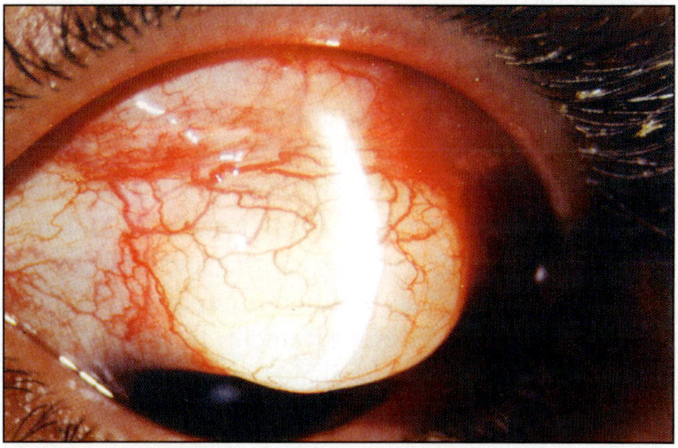

Figure 29: Tight Tenon's cyst 6 weeks following trabeculectomy with 5-FU, IOP 41 mm Hg.

Initial management of encapsulated blebs include antiglaucoma medications in cases of elevated IOP, topical steroids, and digital massage or focal compression of the bleb. Deciding between conservative management (medical) or a surgical revision is usually dependent upon the severity of glaucomatous damage, the level of IOP, and the response to medical management. When surgical revision is needed the simplest technique is to cut the fibrotic wall with a 27-gauge needle or a Ziegler knife. This procedure can be done at the slit-lamp and, if effective, restores aqueous outflow to a larger subconjunctival area. Subconjunctival injections of 5-FU for two weeks after bleb revision increases the chances of success. Alternatively, 0.1 ml of mitomycin-C (0.4 mg/ml) diluted in 0.1 ml of non-preserved lidocaine can be used 30 minutes prior to needling. Excision of the fibrotic tissue has been also proposed.

Visual Loss

Unexplained loss of central visual field (i.e.,"wipe out") after glaucoma surgery is rare. Older patients with advanced visual field defects affecting the central field, with split fixation, are at increased risk. Early undiagnosed postoperative IOP spikes and severe postoperative hypotony have been suspected causes for "wipe-out".

POSTOPERATIVE COMPLICATIONS OCCURING MONTHS - YEARS AFTER SURGERY

Hypotony Maculopathy Due to Overfiltration

Chronic hypotony after filtration surgery is most commonly due to overfiltration Some patients with persistent hypotony develop loss of central vision secondary to marked irregular folding of the choroid and retina. Initially, these folds are broad and not sharply delineated. They tend to radiate outward in a branching fashion temporally from the optic disc, and concentrically or irregularly nasally to the disc. There may be swelling of the peripapillary choroid simulating papilledema. The retina often shows a series of stellate folds around the center of the fovea. The retinal vessels are tortuous and sometimes engorged **(Figure 30)**. Early detection of this condition is important because correction of the cause will usually result in visual improvement. In cases of prolonged hypotony permanent pigmented lines, caused by changes in the retinal pigment epithelium, occur in the macular area and nasally.

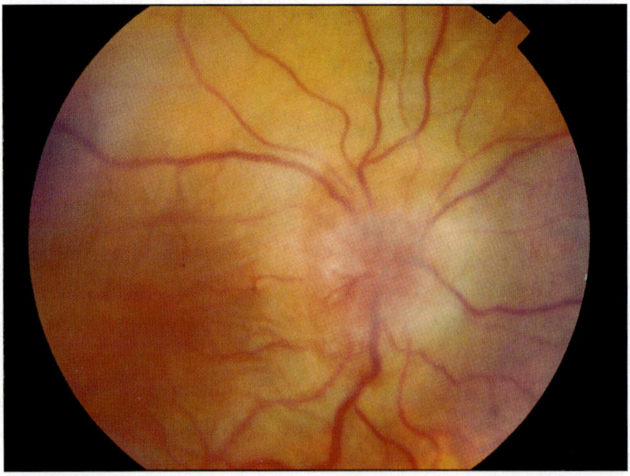

Figure 30: FOptic nerve swelling, hypotony maculopathy following over filtration.

The incidence of hypotony maculopathy after glaucoma surgery has increased with the use of antifibrotic agents. The maculopathy is most likely to occur in young myopic patients, who may have a sclera less rigid and more susceptible to swelling and contraction. Injection of autologous blood into the bleb to reduce overfiltration or to treat bleb leaks after filtering surgery has been reported. Inflammatory cells and serum proteins from the injected blood may accelerate the inflammatory and healing process, which decreases filtration. Approximately 0.2 to 0.5 ml of venous blood from the patient's arm (extracted with a 25-gauge needle in a tuberculin syringe) are injected into and around the filtering bleb with a 30-gauge needle **(Figure 31)**. Possible complications include hyphema, **(Figures 32 – 33)** endophthalmitis, increase in IOP requiring surgical intervention, and bleb failure.

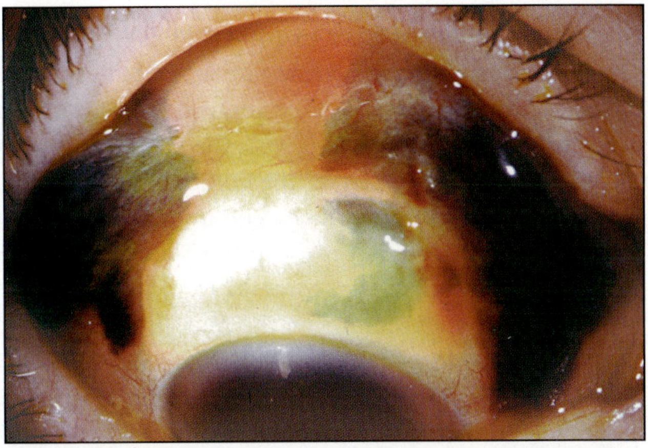

Figure 31: Autologous blood injection immediately postoperative. V.A. 20/80 pre-op, 4 mm Hg.

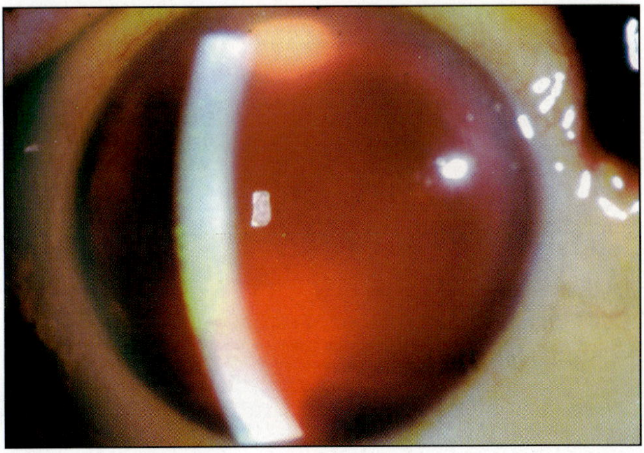

Figure 32: Hyphema immediately following autologous blood injection.

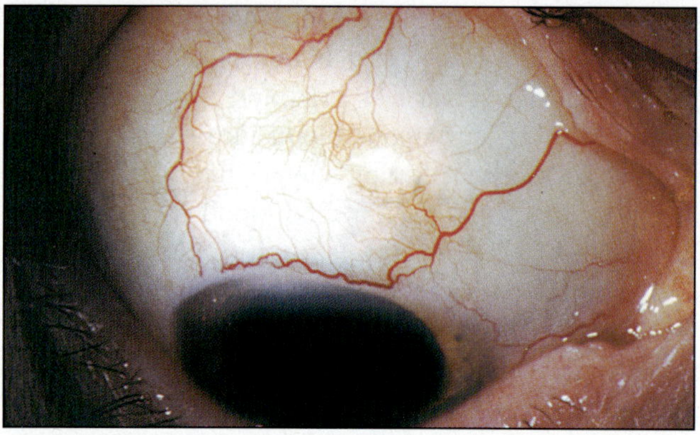

Figure 33: One month following autologous blood injection, IOP 10 mm Hg, V.A. 20/20.

Nd:YAG thermal laser treatment of overfiltering and leaking blebs has been described, although the success rate is limited. It is best done under regional anesthesia. For this procedure the continuous-wave mode is required. Energy levels range between 3.0 and 4.0 J, with the laser offset between 0.9 and 1.2 mm, and the aiming beam focused in the conjunctival epithelium. The goal is to induce whitening and wrinkling of the conjunctival epithelium. A grid pattern of 30 to 40 spots of laser placed over the entire bleb. Postoperatively oral aqueous suppressants and a compressive or "torpedo" (i.e., cotton plug placed directly over the bleb surface) patch are used during the first 48 hours.

Finally, surgical revision for overfiltering blebs may be needed **(Figure 34)**. Resuturing the scleral flap and scleral patch grafting have been successfully used in cases with hypotony maculopathy associated with overfiltering filtering bleb. Alternatively, mattress sutures anchored behind the bleb in episclera and anteriorly in the cornea can be used to compress the bleb. Cataract surgery in eyes with some lens opacities, without using postoperative steroids may improve hypotony.

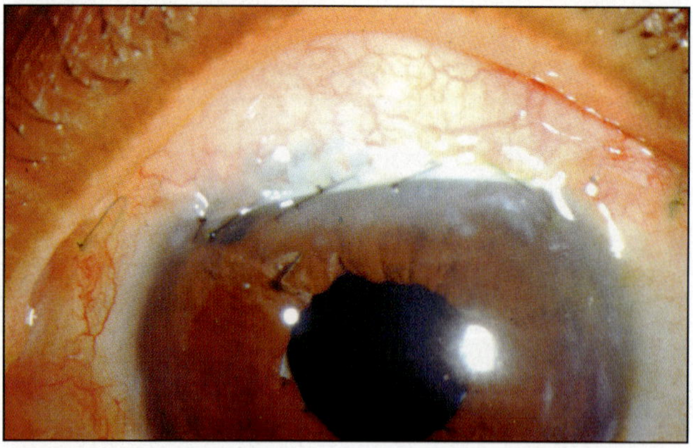

Figure 34: Surgical revision for overfiltering bleb, 3 days post-op. IOP pre-op 2 mm Hg, post-op 14 mm Hg.

Hypotony Due to Cyclodialysis Cleft

Chronic hypotony may occur after inadvertent creation of a cyclodialysis cleft. It can be associated with poor vision and hypotony maculopathy, and with no visible choroidal detachment. The anterior chamber can be formed or shallow, and there is no leak. Cyclodialisis clefts can be diagnosed by gonioscopy **(Figure 35)** and by high-resolution ultrasound biomicroscopy. (ciliary body detachment posterior to the scleral spur may not be visible on gonioscopy and can be diagnosed by high resolution ultrasound biomicroscopy **(Figure 36)** – *Editor*).

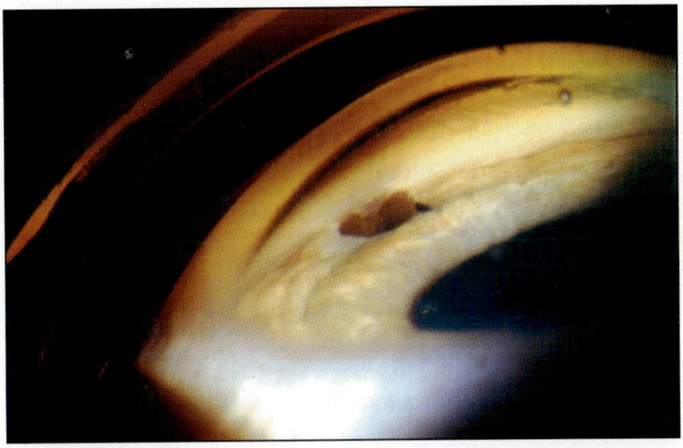

Figure 35: Inadvertent cyclodialysis cleft following cataract surgery causing hypotony, IOP of 4 mm Hg.

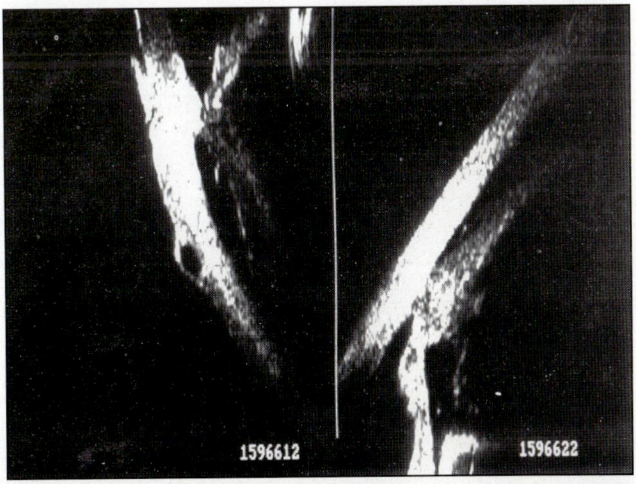

Figure 36: Ciliary body detachment posterior to the scleral spur demonstrated by high resolution ultrasound biomicroscopy (UBM). UBM performed by Dr. Jackson Coleman *Editor*)

Treatment

Argon laser treatment can be used in an attempt to seal the cyclodialysis cleft. Laser settings are 100-200 mm spot sizes, 1-2 W power, and 0.1 sec duration. Regional anesthesia is usually required. The entire available scleral surface, starting in the depths of the cleft, and the choroid and ciliary body are treated. Following laser treatment the IOP should be monitored. Trans-scleral cryotherapy can be also tried.

If laser or cryotherapy is not effective, the ciliary body can be sutured directly to the sclera. A thick scleral flap extending 4 mm posteriorly is raised at the limbus overlying the detached ciliary body. Air or viscoelastic is injected into the anterior chamber. The remaining sclera is incised 1 mm posterior to the scleral spur. At this point, the cyclodialysis cleft is directly visualized. Then, interrupted 10/0 nylon sutures are passed from the anterior lip of sclera, then through the underlying ciliary body, avoiding the iris root, and again back through the posterior scleral lip. The superficial scleral flap is sutured back into place. Postoperative treatment include cycloplegics and, if necessary, aqueous suppressants.

Late Bleb Leak

Late bleb leaks can occur months or years after filtration surgery. Leaks are more likely to occur in avascular, thin blebs, which are seen more frequently when antimetabolites are used. Leakage of the filtering bleb can be associated with hypotony, shallow-flat anterior chamber and choroidal detachment, and may increase the chances for bleb infection and subsequent endophthalmitis **(Figure 37)**.

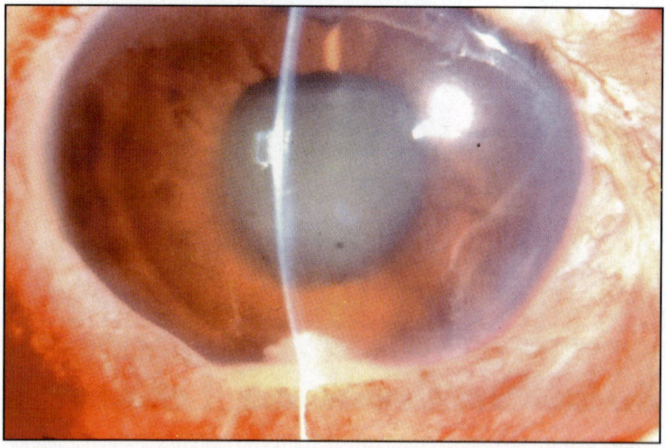

Figure 37: Endophthalmitis following a trabeculectomy. V.A. decreased to hand motion over a 24-hour period.

The need and urgency of the management of bleb leaks depend on several factors. Some cases with history of previous bleb-related infections, shallow-flat anterior chamber, or reduced vision should be always treated. However, if there are no complications, such as in late leaks with formed blebs, normal intraocular pressure, good central vision and without previous episodes of bleb-related infection, the leak may not require therapy. Observation is possible to allow spontaneous closure of the leak. Pharmacological medical treatment with agents that decrease aqueous secretion (topical betablockers and/or CAI) and discontinuation of topical steroids, with or without patching, may help the spontaneous closure of these defects by reducing flow of aqueous through the fistula. Prophylactic broad spectrum antibiotic coverage, alternating different antibiotics, may be used. Patient education regarding symptoms of bleb-related ocular infection is crucial for prompt diagnosis and management.

Therapeutic modalities to treat late leaking blebs include pressure patching and bandage contact lens (see above), injection of autologous blood (see above), thermal Nd:YAG laser (see above), and surgical revision. When surgical revision is required, it is important to attempt to save the established initial filtration site. Due to the friable nature of the conjunctiva in long-established filtering blebs, it is often impossible to close the defect directly with sutures and, therefore, healthy conjunctival tissue is needed. First, the ischemic and thin-walled bleb tissue is denuded of conjunctival epithelium with mild cauterization to allow long-term adherence of the grafted conjunctiva. Fresh conjunctiva adjacent to the bleb is then mobilized to cover the previous filtration site by rotational, sliding or free conjunctival grafts. The conjunctiva is sutured over the previously abraded peripheral cornea with 10-0 nylon providing a watertight seal. Alternatively, radial compressing (delimiting) mattress sutures can be placed over the conjunctival surface, anchored behind the bleb in episclera and anteriorly in the cornea to isolate a leak from the remaining bleb and aid healing. Amniotic membrane can be used as an alternative substrate. With these methods bleb function can be usually preserved.

Bleb-Related Ocular Infection

Ocular infections related to filtration procedures can occur months to years after the initial surgery. Inferior filtering blebs, thin, localized and avascular blebs (more commonly seen after using antifibrotic agents) and leaks increase the probability of bleb-related ocular infection.

Bleb-related ocular infections can affect three compartments: the subconjunctival space (Stage I), the anterior segment (Stage II), and the vitreous cavity (Stage III). Usually the spread of infection proceeds in that order. Because the fluid within the bleb is continuous with the anterior chamber an infection of the bleb affecting the subconjunctival space ("blebitis") has a very real potential to rapidly

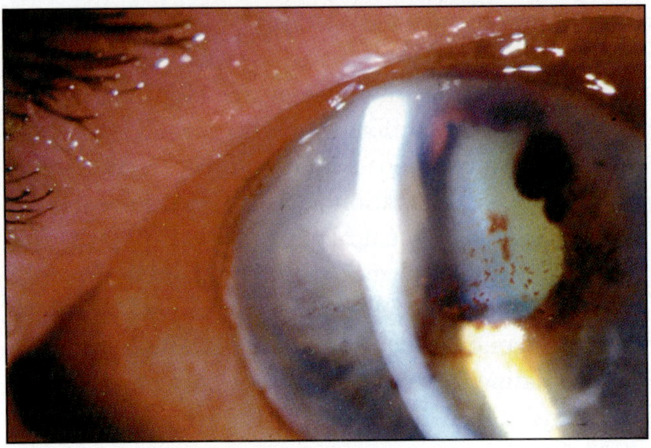

Figure 38: Cataract progression following a trabeculectomy complicated by hemorrhage into the anterior chamber.

spread posteriorly. The bacteria that cause bleb-related endophthalmitis almost certainly arise from the ocular flora. The most commonly involved organisms include Streptococcus species, H. influenza and Staphylococcus species.

Patients with bleb-related ocular infection usually present with ocular pain, blurred vision, tearing, redness and discharge. Examination reveals conjunctival and ciliary injection, most intense around the bleb edge, and purulent discharge. There may be periorbital chemosis. In Stage II and III anterior chamber reaction is noted, including frequently keratic precipitates, corneal edema and, in some cases, hypopyon **(Figure 38)**. The bleb typically has a milky-white appearance with loss of clarity. A positive Seidel's test is common, and some patients may have a substantial leak, hypotony, and even flat anterior chamber. Alternatively, an increased IOP is possible due to internal closure of sclerostomy site with purulence and debris.

Vitreous reaction is not evident in early stages (Stage I and II) but, untreated, the infection spreads to the posterior segment (Stage III). If the media is not clear (e.g., dense cataract), B-mode ultrasonography can be helpful to detect involvement of the retrolental area.

The general principles that guide the management of ocular infections apply to this condition. It is important to identify the organism responsible. A conjunctival sample is routinely collected, stained and cultured. However, conjunctival culture in the etiologic diagnosis of bleb-related endophthalmitis has very little value. A vitreous sample should be obtained in stage III.

In stage I (blebitis without anterior chamber reaction) frequent topical application of a commercially available broad-spectrum antibiotic can be used, with very close supervision. Steroids can be considered to reduce the intense inflammation and preserve bleb integrity when the infection appears to be controlled. In stage II, (the anterior segment but not the posterior segment is involved), treatment with fortified topical antibiotics around the clock is advisable. Topical fortified cefazoline or vancomycin associated with fortified tobramycin, moxyfloxacin or amikacin are likely to be effective against most gram-positive and gram-negative microorganisms. Additional systemic antibiotics can be used. In stage III (bleb-related endophthalmitis) intravitreal antibiotics are required, administered either through a pars plana injection at the time of sampling or associated with a vitrectomy. We are currently using 1 mg of vancomycin (10 mg/ml) and 400 mgr. of amikacin (5 mg/ml). Systemic antibiotics can be used. However, the Endophthalmitis Vitrectomy Study did not show any benefits of using systemic antibiotics in patients with endophthamitis after cataract surgery.

After resolution of the infection the function of the filtration bleb may be impaired. Other possible complications include corneal edema, cataract, vitreoretinal traction and retinal toxicity from the bacteria's toxins or the antibiotics. The visual outcome is usually good in cases with anterior segment involvement and poor when the vitreous is involved, especially with virulent bacteria such as Streptococci, coagulase-positive Staphylococci, and gram-negative organisms.

Prevention of bleb-related ocular infection is important. Some ophthalmologists use long-term topical antibiotics after filtration procedures, although the efficacy of this regimen has been questioned. It seems reasonable to use long-term antibiotics in some cases of leaking blebs, inferior blebs, or recurrent bleb-related infections. Conjunctivitis and blepharitis should be treated promptly, and soft contact lens wear should be avoided. Patient education about early symptoms of infection is currently the most important approach to minimize the chances of severe visual loss.

Cataract Formation Following Filtration Surgery

Cataract formation and progression of pre-existing cataract can occur after filtration procedures. Lens opacification although is less frequent, still is the main cause of early visual loss after filtration surgery. The reported incidence varies from 2% to 47%. For example, in the Normal Tension Glaucoma Study, after 5 years of follow-up the incidence of cataract was 14% in the control group and 38% in the treated group, with the highest incidence in those whose treatment included filtration surgery.

Intraoperative lenticular trauma is possible, and can be recognized shortly after surgery. Intraoperative or postoperative flat anterior chamber with lens-corneal touch rapidly precipitates cataract formation. Other probable risk factors include age, presence of exfoliation, use of air to reform the anterior chamber, profound hypotony, use of miotics, topical steroids and inflammation.

Cataract extraction can be associated with a partial impairment of the function of the filtering bleb. Phacoemulsification of the lens with a corneal incision is the preferred method. Postoperative application of 5-FU or Mitomycin can be considered. If the control of IOP is sub-optimal, a combined phacoemulsification and filtration procedure may be a preferred choice.

Editorial Comment

Several complications after glaucoma surgery continue to be a serious cause of surgical failure in patients with complex glaucoma. Improvement in surgical technique, especially with the judicial use of antiproliferatives and enhancing the biocompatibility of tube implants, may further reduce these risks with filtration surgery.

Samuel Boyd, MD. Editor-in-Chief.

Bibliography

1. O'Brart DP, Shiew M, Edmunds B. A randomised, prospective study comparing trabeculectomy with viscocanalostomy with adjunctive antimetabolite usage for the management of open angle glaucoma uncontrolled by medical therapy. Br J Ophthalmol. Aug 2004;88(8):1012-7.
2. Wamsley S, Moster MR, Rai S. Results of the use of the Ex-PRESS miniature glaucoma implant in technically challenging, advanced glaucoma cases: a clinical pilot study. Am J Ophthalmol. Dec 2004;138(6):1049-51.
3. Jiraskova N, Rozsival P, Pozlerova J, Ludvikova M, Burova M. Expulsive hemorrhage after glaucoma filtering surgery. Biomed Pap Med Fac Univ Palacky Olomouc Czech Repub. Sep 2009;153(3):221-4.
4. Asrani SG, Wilensky JT. Management of bleb leaks after glaucoma filtering surgery. Use of autologous fibrin tissue glue as an alternative. Ophthalmology. Feb 1996;103(2):294-8.
5. Ulrich GG, Proia AD, Shields MB. Clinicopathologic features and surgical management of dissecting glaucoma filtering blebs. Ophthalmic Surg Lasers. Feb 1997;28(2):151-5.
6. [Guideline] AGIS Investigators. The advanced glaucoma intervention study (AGIS): 7. The relationship between control of intraocular pressure and visual field deterioration. Am J Ophthalmol. Oct 2000;130(4):429-40.
7. Bellows AR, Chylack LT Jr, Hutchinson BT. Choroidal detachment. Clinical manifestation, therapy and mechanism of formation. Ophthalmology. Nov 1981;88(11):1107-15.
8. Cohn H. Indications for trabeculectomy in open angle glaucoma. Bull Soc Belge Ophtalmol. 1992;244:155-60.
9. Costa VP, Smith M, Spaeth GL, et al. Loss of visual acuity after trabeculectomy. Ophthalmology. May 1993;100(5):599-612.
10. Dietlein TS. Perspectives in glaucoma surgery. Ophthalmologe. Feb 2002;99(2):74-84.
11. Elliot RH. A Treatise on Glaucoma. New York: Hodder & Stoughton; 1922.
12. Hamard P, Lachkar Y. Non penetrating filtering surgery, evolution and results. J Fr Ophthalmol. May 2002;25(5):527-36.
13. Hirvela H, Laatikainen L. Visual acuity in a population aged 70 years or older; prevalence and causes of visual impairment. Acta Ophthalmol Scand. Apr 1995;73(2):99-104.
14. Nouri-Mahdavi K, Hoffman D, Gaasterland D. Prediction of visual field progression in glaucoma. Invest Ophthalmol Vis Sci. Dec 2004;45(12):4346-51.
15. Sacca S, Marletta A, Pascotto A. Daily tonometric curves after cataract surgery. Br J Ophthalmol. Jan 2001;85(1):24-9.
16. Shields MB. Reflections and projections on crossing the millennium: Tenth American Glaucoma Society Lecture honoring Marvin L. Sears, MD. J Glaucoma. Apr 2001;10(2):136-43.
17. Weinreb RN, Zangwill L, Berry CC. Detection of glaucoma with scanning laser polarimetry. Arch Ophthalmol. Dec 1998;116(12):1583-9.

Index